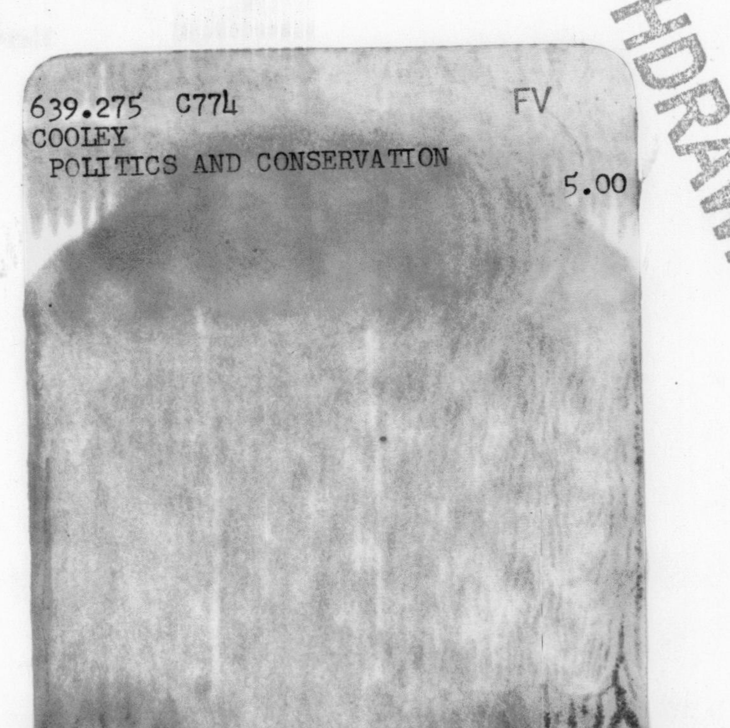

POLITICS AND CONSERVATION

POLITICS *and*

POLITICS AND CONSERVATION

The Decline of the Alaska Salmon

Richard A. Cooley

Harper & Row, Publishers
New York, Evanston, and London

A study sponsored by The Conservation Foundation

FIRST EDITION

LIBRARY OF CONGRESS CATALOG CARD NUMBER: 63-16545

Contents

Part Three. Sequence and Consequence

Illustrations

Charts

Figure

PHOTOGRAPHS

Acknowledgments

I AM DEEPLY GRATEFUL to The Conservation Foundation of New York City whose support and cooperation made this research possible. My gratitude extends to Professor Lyle E. Craine of the School of Natural Resources at the University of Michigan, under whose guidance and advice the study was formulated and carried on; to Drs. Stanley A. Cain, Richard L. Meier, Robert H. Pealy, and Dean Stanley G. Fontanna of the same institution, who provided helpful comments and criticisms; to Dr. James A. Crutchfield of the Department of Economics at the University of Washington, and Mr. Wallace D. Bowman of the Office of the Governor in Juneau, Alaska, who read and commented incisively on the first draft; and finally to Senator Ernest Gruening of Alaska, who reviewed the manuscript and kindly agreed to write an introduction. Valuable assistance was received from many others in government and industry who helped me to understand the history and evolution of the problems dealt with in the study.

I am most indebted to my wife, whose encouragement and assistance was indispensable.

RICHARD A. COOLEY

Juneau, Alaska
March, 1963

Foreword

by Stanley A. Cain
Charles Lathrop Pack Professor of Conservation
The University of Michigan

Around the world there are monuments to the failure of one-sided attacks on human problems.

In Nigeria a British-sponsored riverside brush-control program to reduce the tsetse fly was dropped when British influence was withdrawn, not because the program had not reduced sleeping sickness and improved the health of local people, but because the tribes never understood the biological cause of disease and still held to their traditional belief in control by spirits. In several American states scientific management of deer and elk herds is not possible because wildlife biologists do not have a free hand. Wildlife laws and administrative policies have other ingredients, such as politics, intergovernmental jurisdictional disputes, small but vocal groups with vested personal interests, and well-meaning, sentimental lovers of nature who find reprehensible the shooting of female and young animals.

The integrated management of the several natural resources of a geographic complex requires cooperation among several publics, each of which has its own limited understandings and objectives. And this cooperation, which would optimize the net benefits from all resources, will not necessarily maximize the benefit from any single resource. Also, a single resource, such as the water in lakes, streams, and aquifers of a major watershed, has its distinct and frequently conflicting uses for agriculture, forestry, fish and wildlife, recreation, manufacturing, power production, and domestic and municipal purposes. Such complex natural-resource problems have no *single* solutions. As the saying goes, "All cats are gray at night," but, as we shall see, under illumination some cats still are gray.

Although there always are basic scientific problems to be solved in the development and use of natural resources, science alone will not solve a single resource-use problem. The same thing can be said of the political, public agency, economic, and intangible ingredients: No one approach will do. All of which brings us to Richard A. Cooley's study of the ninety-year history of Alaska salmon.

Rather than placing the blame for what happened to salmon, Dr. Cooley has identified the main reasons why it happened the way it did. In order to do this adequately, he gives full consideration to biological, social, and economic factors as well as the purely political ones. We can, I think, but agree with him. What happened in the political arena can be understood fully *only* when these other important elements are understood and their roles integrated with the political one. Specialists tend to see only black or white cats. Cooley's cats are hybrids—black and white mixed, sometimes gray.

The author makes no specific policy recommendations about what *ought* to be done. This is not his task. Yet a careful reading of the book will provide policy-makers and citizens, scientists and businessmen, with a firm foundation for reaching more rational decisions about Alaska salmon than has characterized history. What is more important, this study has general meaning for the management of natural resources not only in Alaska, but throughout the world. It will be illuminating and useful to thoughtful persons of many special interests: politicians and administrators of public agencies, certainly, but fishery biologists, economists, students of government, historians, and general conservationists, also. The book is enlightening to the lay reader—the decent citizen frequently at a loss to understand the conflict of forces seemingly beyond his control that affect the course of public policy.

This study is a scholarly example of the "new conservation" and, although it will make him shudder, I would say that Dr. Cooley is a "neo-conservationist."

Introduction

by Senator Ernest Gruening

America's greatest fishery resource was the Pacific salmon. Along the Pacific coast, increasingly northward from California, and in its greatest abundance in Alaska, salmon would, during the summer months, return, from absences at sea of lengths varying according to species, to the rivers and lakes where they were born to spawn and die. It was an American resource in the very special sense that, unlike other fish such as cod or tuna caught in the open ocean in international waters, the Pacific salmon is anadromous and is taken in American coastal waters near the mouths of the streams to which they are returning.

Alaska's aboriginal culture was based on salmon. It amply nourished the Indians of the northwest coast and formed the basis of their totemic culture.

The commercial exploitation of this great resource began in Alaska in 1878 with the establishment of two canneries. Less than a quarter of a century later, a few far-visioned scientists serving the United States government foresaw the danger of its possible depletion and near-extinction unless the resource was adequately safeguarded by conservation measures. Their Cassandra-like warnings fell on deaf ears.

Richard A. Cooley tells how and why it happened. His book is a factual, authoritative, and fascinating account of how greed, ignorance, politics, and federal mismanagement combined to bring this great resource almost to the vanishing point.

It is, in fact, the story of a colossal failure; the failure of a United States government agency entrusted with the high responsibility of conserving this great natural heritage to perform its function. The fact is that during the years of their trusteeship, the federal regulatory agencies—since 1940 the Fish and Wildlife Service—instead of regulating the industry, were regulated and controlled by it. The twenty years of Fish and Wildlife control, from 1940 until statehood in 1959, were the most disastrous of all. These were the years of the decline and near-extinction of the Pacific salmon in Alaska.

Meanwhile, in neighboring British Columbia, the same, though far less abundant, resource was successfully conserved.

Despite the unceasing protests of Alaskans, the biennial memorials of the Territorial Legislature, the repeated efforts of Alaska's voteless delegates in the Congress, the concerted and valid criticisms of Alaska's fishermen, the Interior Department's Fish and Wildlife Service was utterly oblivious to these pleas and presided over the steady decrease of the salmon resource until, in 1959, the last year of federal control, it reached the lowest point in sixty years—the lowest since the days when commercial exploitation was in its infancy. During Fish and Wildlife control, the decline in the annual pack tells the story.

Year	*Total Cases*
1941	6,906,503
1942	5,089,109
1943	5,396,509
1944	4,877,796
1945	4,341,120
1946	3,971,109
1947	4,302,466
1948	4,010,612
1949	4,391,051
1950	3,272,643
1951	3,484,468
1952	3,574,128
1953	2,925,570

1954	3,207,154
1955	2,457,969
1956	2,950,354
1957	2,441,894
1958	2,948,371
1959	1,600,000

During those sixty years, the absentee-owned canned salmon industry was opposing all conservation measures proposed at various times by conscientious government officials who found themselves overwhelmed by political pressure and alternative threats which would put an end to their public career or blandishments with offers of positions with the industry.

The industry likewise opposed all measures to increase the political autonomy of Alaska. Its lobby in Washington was sufficiently powerful to deny Alaska, in the Organic Act of 1912, the management of the fishery resource—not denied any other American territory—although it failed in its attempt to prevent the territory of Alaska from taxing the fish products. It devised a unique and unprecedented political structure, making the legislature easy to control, which it did with skill and without scruple. Bribery and pay-offs were practiced; financial rewards were available for the complaisant, and they prospered by betraying their trust as public servants. Incidental to the lobby's manipulations was the throttling of Alaska's economy. Its agents went far to prescribe Alaska's governmental income and expenditures. Its unscrupulous and oppressive tactics were a major factor in awakening the people of Alaska to the need for statehood—and in their getting it.

It is a tragic and sordid story, the consequences of which will long be with the people of Alaska and the nation. Cooley tells it factually, objectively—with the added strength of understatement.

The Legacy: An Introduction

UNDER THE AMERICAN SYSTEM of federalism the states have the power to regulate fisheries within the waters under their respective jurisdictions. Historically this has been defined to include coastal waters to a distance of three miles from the shore. In the case of waters surrounding territory acquired by the United States after the formation of the Union, the power to regulate the fisheries remains with the federal government to be held "in trust" for the benefit of the people of the state subsequently created out of such territory.[1] However, in passing organic acts setting up organized territories from newly acquired lands, Congress saw fit to give new territorial governments varying degrees of regulatory authority to manage and control their own fishery resources. The only exception has been the territory of Alaska. Despite diligent opposition on the part of the people of the territory, when the Alaska Organic Act was passed on August 24, 1912, providing for a legislature and a limited amount of self-government, it contained a provision specifically prohibiting the newly created Territorial Legislature from passing any laws that would "alter, amend, modify

[1] For a full review of these legal aspects with case citations see: *American Jurisprudence,* Vol. 22, pp. 673 ff.

or repeal any federal laws relating to the fisheries of Alaska.[2] Consequently, management of the Alaska salmon resource has been the sole responsibility of the federal government from the time Alaska was purchased from Russia in 1867 until January 1, 1960, one year after Alaska became a full-fledged state.[3]

Since this was the only instance in which the federal government had regulatory authority over a fishery resource, it provided a unique and challenging opportunity to formulate and execute a rational conservation program that could be held up to the individual states as a model for the handling of the complex problems of fishery conservation. Indeed, during the early formulative years of the federal salmon-management program in Alaska, officials frequently gave lip service to this objective. At one time concrete proposals were discussed as to the advisability of having the federal government take over complete control of the salmon-conservation program along with the entire West coast of the United States because of the difficulties the various states were having. Those backing the idea believed that the federal government, with its superior financial resources and its broader view of the public interest, would be in a much stronger position to finance costly programs of research, to take the necessary coercive regulatory actions, and to withstand the political pressures from local interests who were striving and competing to maximize their annual returns from the fishery. While none of these proposals progressed very far, they nevertheless indicate what high expectations were held for the success of the federal salmon-management program in Alaska.

Optimism was expressed as late as 1939 in an exhaustive study of the North Pacific fisheries published by the American Institute of Public Relations. In comparing the federal salmon-management program in Alaska with similar programs under other political jurisdictions along the Pacific coast the following conclusion was drawn:

---

[2] 37 Stat. 512, Sec. 3.

[3] The Alaska Statehood Act was passed by the 85th Congress on July 7, 1958 (72 Stat. 339). Statehood became effective under the Act on January 1, 1958, and full control over the fisheries was turned over to the state on January 1, 1960.

The effort has been unsuccessful in California, and, so far, of questionable success in Washington and Oregon although it has probably prevented even greater decline. Alaska, however, seems to enjoy conservation policies and techniques which should make its salmon reserves part of the heritage of succeeding generations.[4]

At the time this statement was written salmon production from the waters of Alaska had just passed its apex. What followed was a continuous downward spiral in annual catches that became progressively more serious as the years went by. By the 1950s the salmon industry, once the chief mainstay of the Alaska economy, had toppled to near ruin.

In January 1960, William A. Egan, Alaska's first elected governor, made the following statement in his message to the Joint Assembly of the First Alaska State Legislature:

> On January 1 of this year, Alaska's Department of Fish and Game was handed the depleted remnants of what was once a rich and prolific fishery. From a peak of three-quarters of a billion pounds in 1936, production dropped in 1959 to its lowest in 60 years.
>
> On these ruins of a once great resource, the department must rebuild. Our gain is that we can profit by studying the destructive practices, mistakes and omissions of the past.
>
> The revival of the commercial fisheries is an absolute imperative. The livelihood of thousands of fishermen and the very existence of many communities scattered along thousands of miles of continental and island coastline depends upon improvement of the fisheries. To this end we will give our best efforts.[5]

This is the legacy given the people of Alaska.

The purpose of this study is to trace the development of federal policies for the conservation of the Alaska salmon resource in an effort to understand how the policies were formulated and executed, what major forces shaped their ultimate content, and why they have been so ineffective in maintaining the resource at a high level of production. The purpose is not to censure or attempt to lay blame for what has happened to the resource in the past. Nothing constructive would be accomplished by this. The ultimate question is whether the state can succeed where the federal government

[4] Homer E. Gregory and Kathleen Barnes, *North Pacific Fisheries* (San Francisco: American Institute of Pacific Relations, 1939), p. 77.

[5] Message by Governor William A. Egan to the Joint Assembly of the First Alaska State Legislature, Second Session, Supplement to House and Senate Journals, January 26, 1960, Second Day.

failed, a unique question in this day and age when so many public problems have tended to gravitate in exactly the opposite direction for solution. By telling the story of this particular set of natural-resource policy decisions more fully than it has been told before, it is hoped that some new light will be shed on the current problems and issues confronting the state of Alaska in the attempt to rehabilitate the resource to its former productive potential.

Since the beginning of commercial exploitation many persons and groups have been interested in how the salmon resource was to be developed and conserved: fishermen, cannery workers, salmon packers and brokers, bankers, suppliers, federal and territorial officials, and other individuals and representatives of organizations of one kind or another. Some have been highly organized and well financed, others have been handicapped economically or politically or in both respects, but all have sought to influence the formation and execution of the policies for the management of the resource. As a study in public policy, this research is concerned primarily with these people, their organization into groups, and their behavior *vis-à-vis* this particular natural resource: how they acted and reacted in their effort to develop, manage, and conserve it. It is recognized, however, that the formation of public policy cannot be understood solely in the political context, for there are important physical, economic, and institutional features which not only influence the participants in the political process, but also delimit the environment within which policy decisions can be made.

Part One of the study analyzes this environmental setting to determine the major factors which have conditioned the structure of the industry and the resulting pattern of exploitation. The research method used here is primarily statistical and economic analysis. Part Two traces the historical development of the federal conservation program, emphasizing the major issues and conflicts that evolved, the attitudes and activities of the various interest groups, and the public policies that resulted. This is based on a thorough examination of the written record as found in congressional hearings, committee reports, the *Congressional Record,* official reports of government agencies, enacted laws and policy statements, newspapers and trade journals, and the writings, addresses, letters and reports of persons and organizations involved in the policy-formulating process. It has been supplemented by correspondence and interviews with persons in both government and business who had knowledge of particular aspects of the study. A final source of information stems from personal experience, work, and travels of the author, who has been a resident Alaskan during the last ten years. Part Three presents the conclusions and evaluates their implications in terms of the probable future of the resource under state government administration.

PART ONE

THE PATTERN OF EXPLOITATION

FIGURE 1. MAJOR FISHING REGIONS OF ALASKA

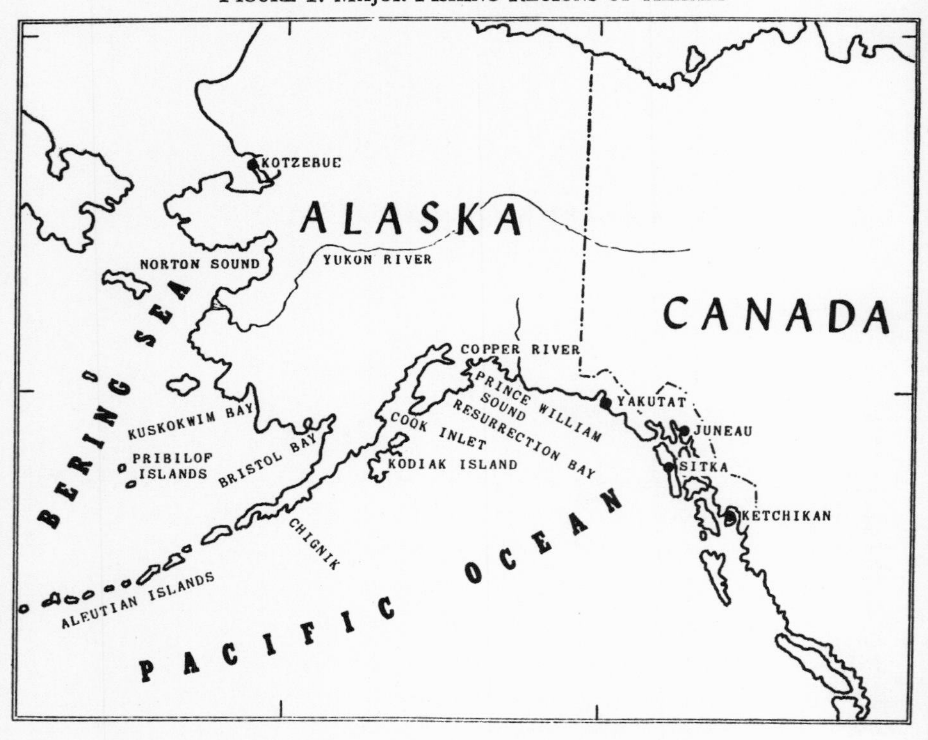

1 *The Resource*

EACH YEAR DURING THE spring, summer, and fall, mature Pacific salmon rise from the broad reaches of the ocean —the exact time depending on the species—and instinctively head landward toward the stream or river of their origin where they will spawn and die. As the fish approach land they form into schools which move along the coastline in fairly well-defined routes. At the mouths of the streams they congregate in hordes. Physically they are at their prime, having a tremendous amount of stored energy in the form of body fats and tissues sufficient to maintain them during the last and most arduous part of their journey. When stream conditions such as temperature, flow, turbulence, and objects for visual orientation are right, the fish surge into the swift fresh-water currents and battle their way up rapids, around boulders, and over falls until they reach the spawning beds. Some species go only a short distance upstream before spawning, while others travel hundreds of miles before reaching the headwaters or lakes where they originated. Some of the spawning beds in the Yukon River, for example, are two thousand miles from the sea, and since the time is short between the disappearance of the ice in the spring and its reappearance in the fall, the distance must be covered with great speed. Records show that the fish have made the first fifteen hundred miles in thirty days, a rate of fifty miles a day against the current.[1]

Salmon cease feeding as soon as they are in fresh water, and one of nature's astonishing phenomena is the rapid physiological change and disintegration that takes place once they are in the streams. Some species develop a hook on their snout, while others turn bright red. Their silvery scales become dull and appear to be flaking off; although they are still fortified with great energy, in many cases their flesh may be hanging in strips by the time they reach their destination. At the spawning grounds the fish scoop out shallow nests in the gravel. The female deposits the eggs, which are then fertilized by the male. By swimming back and forth across the nest the fish cover the eggs with coarse gravel. Within a short time both the male and female die, their life cycle completed.[2] When the spawn hatches, the young fingerlings spend varying amounts of time in fresh water, depending upon the species, and then head downstream to the salt-water reaches of the Pacific Ocean where they feed and grow to maturity.

There are five distinct species of Pacific salmon and they range from the Sacramento to the Siberian rivers. These five species belong to a single genus distinct from that of the Atlantic salmon and the true trouts, but they are grouped within the same general family (Salmonidae). The Pacific salmon were first classified by Russian scientists, and their scientific names—*Oncorhynchus tschawytscha, Oncorhynchus gorbusca,* etc.—are primarily derived from Russian or from local Siberian native languages. For the purposes of this study, however, the salmon will be referred to by their popular names: the red, the king, the silver, the pink, and the chum. Each species has separate characteristics and is of different commercial value.

The Alaska red salmon, also known as the sockeye in British Columbia and Puget Sound, is the most valuable species commercially. Its flesh is bright red and rich in oil, and it retains both color and flavor under nearly all conditions of processing. This species,

---

[1] Brian Curtis, *The Life Story of the Fish* (New York: Harcourt, Brace, and Co., 1949), p. 188.

[2] Females may make several nests and usually survive from several days to a week or more after all eggs are laid. Males may perform several spawning acts with one or more females and can survive up to several weeks after the final one.

the first to be caught commercially in Alaska, is the fish on which the great salmon-canning industry of the Pacific coast was built. The catch is used almost exclusively for canning. The reds range along the coast from northern California to Alaska and westward to Japan. Two of the most productive red salmon fisheries in the world are the Frazer River in British Columbia and the Bristol Bay region in Alaska. The red salmon is a small fish with an average weight of six to seven pounds. Its life cycle ranges from four years in the southern districts to five or six years, and occasionally to seven or eight years, in the north. The reds have the peculiar habit of running only in rivers with lakes along their courses or at their headwaters, and the young generally spend about a year in a lake before going to sea.

The largest of the five species is the king salmon, also called the chinook or spring salmon in other regions. The king averages around twenty pounds but weights in excess of one hundred pounds have occurred. It is caught the length of the coastal region from California to Alaska and is also found along the Asiatic coast as far south as northern China. Its life history is more complicated than the red salmon's. Some kings migrate to salt water shortly after they emerge from the spawning beds, while others may spend a full year in fresh water before migrating. It will be anywhere from three to seven years, depending upon the conditions, before they mature and return to spawn. Kings are important both as a food and as a sport fish, and although fewer are caught commercially than any other species it is the most valuable in terms of price per pound. In the early days of the industry the king was used primarily for canning, but in more recent times the majority of the catch has gone to the fresh- and frozen-food markets where it commands a much higher price.

The silver salmon or coho, as it is frequently called, averages to weigh around seven pounds, with maximum weights of up to thirty pounds. It is found as far south as San Francisco and appears in most of the rivers up the coast through Alaska and west to Japan on the Asiatic side. Like the king it is important both commercially and as a sport fish, but since its flesh is lighter in color than that of either the red or the king it commands a lower price on the markets. The silver, whose life history is less complete than those of the preceding species, generally spends one or two years in the

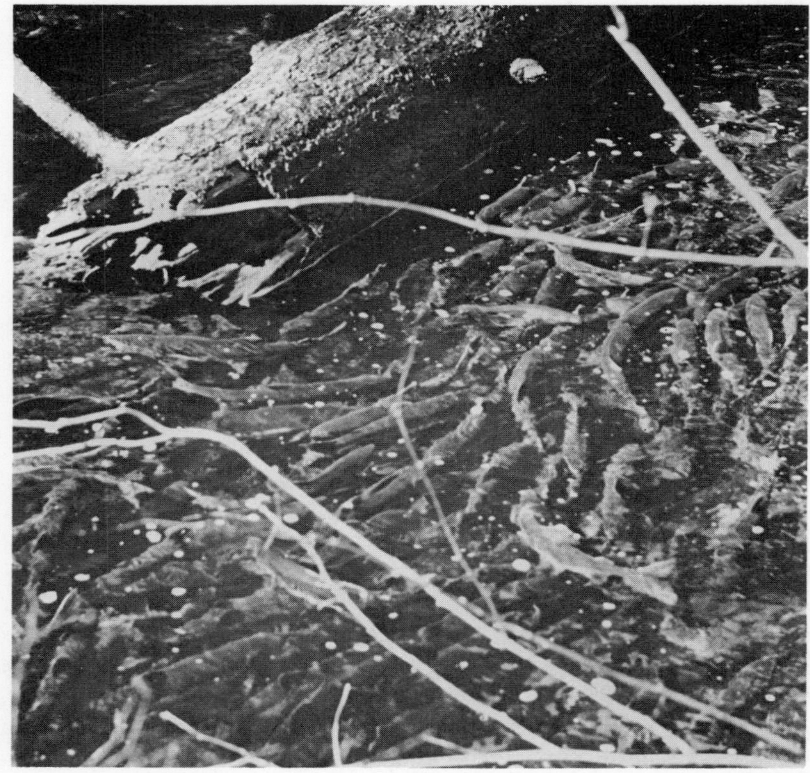

U.S. Fish & Wildlife Service

Pink salmon on spawning bed.

nursing stream and then two years in salt water before returning home to spawn. The major portion of the catch is used in the fresh- and cured-fish trade.

The pink salmon, also known as the humpback, is the smallest and most abundant of all species. It averages around four pounds, with an eleven-pound maximum. The flesh is pale pink and has a lower oil content than the flesh of the red, king, or silver salmon; consequently it has a lower per unit commercial value. This species has a simple two-year life cycle, with the young passing out to sea soon after they are hatched. The pink is seldom found south of Puget Sound. The largest runs occur in Asia along the Siberian coast, and pinks are also caught in great abundance in southeast

Alaska. They have been found on the Arctic drainages from the Mackenzie River to Siberia. The pink is considered an important sport fish and is sought commercially primarily for canning.

The chum salmon is the least valuable of the five species. Its flesh is light yellow and the fish usually weighs between eight and fifteen pounds at maturity. The species is distributed along the Pacific coast from Oregon to northern Japan, with the main commercial runs concentrating between Puget Sound and southeast Alaska. They are also found in large numbers on the Kamchatka Peninsula on the Asiatic coast. Most chums are three or four years old at spawning. The majority of the chum catch is used in the canning industry.

Nutritional and biochemical studies of salmon indicate that it is particularly valuable as a protein food.[3] It contains more of the tissue-building substance than many other protein foods, and since there is little variation in the protein content of the several salmon species the lower-priced pinks and chums are nutritionally important. Salmon also contains other dietetic necessities in important quantities of Vitamin D and provides significant amounts of Vitamins A and G. It is a good source of iodine, calcium, and phosphorous and provides smaller quantities of other important minerals. There is considerable variation in fat content of the different species, but as a whole salmon does not rank high as a fat food.

As a renewable natural resource the salmon reserves represent a segment of national wealth which if wisely used can be passed down from generation to generation. Like other valuable resources of its kind, however, a competitive industrial system has made it necessary to place restraints on exploitation in order to assure a future supply. Since only mature salmon on their way back to the spawning grounds are taken in the commercial fishery, many of the complicated management problems of cropping fish of different ages, sizes, and growth rates which plague other sea fisheries are of much less concern; but there are complications which make the problem of conserving the salmon resource extremely difficult.[4]

The anadromous nature of the salmon has made it more easily

---

[3] For a listing of the more important studies see: Homer E. Gregory and Kathleen Barnes, *North Pacific Fisheries* (San Francisco: Institute of Pacific Relations, 1939), Studies of the Pacific, No. 3, p. 144.

[4] Some kings and silvers are taken before they are fully matured and in recent years the Japanese high seas salmon fishery has taken immature fish, but as a whole the statement is true in relation to most other fisheries.

susceptible to commercial exploitation and hence to overfishing than is the case with most marine resources. It is not necessary for the commercial fisherman to take to the high seas in pursuit of the fish. He need only set out his gear at the proper time and place along the coastline and wait for the runs of mature salmon to materialize on their journey to the spawning beds. Under these conditions there is an important correlation between the amount of fishing effort, the amount of the escapement to the spawning beds, and the number of fish that will return in the following cycle. Thus, the effect of the catch on the subsequent supply of the resource is of dominant importance.

This seemingly simple relationship is complicated by a little-understood biological feature of the resource. Salmon have a highly developed homing instinct which leads each fish back to spawn in the stream from which it originated. It was not until well into the present century that scientists recognized and accepted this phenomenon as true, and they are still at a loss to explain how these feats are accomplished. This has been called the parent-stream theory but the word "parent' is misleading, for it has been proved that the fish do not return to the stream of their parents but to the identical tributary stream where they grew up. Thus each tributary maintains its own separate population of salmon with distinct racial characteristics. If a particular stream is cut off by a log jam or effectively depleted through overfishing, the entire race in that stream can be extirpated. If the log jam is eventually removed or fishing controlled to allow escapement to the spawning grounds again, no salmon of the original population will remain to return to those spawning beds. The stream must remain barren and unproductive unless artificially restocked by a new race of hatchery-reared salmon.[5]

For the purposes of conservation each stream must be viewed as a separate unit. Fishing intensity cannot be controlled in a general manner, but must be strictly regulated in each watershed to assure an adequate escapement to each of the tributaries each year. There are about two thousand salmon streams in Alaska which

[5] Some wandering does occur occasionally which may lead to natural restocking of previously barren streams, but this is of little importance except when a very long time span is being considered. (All Alaska salmon races have evolved in the last 10,000 years.)

receive significant amounts of spawning salmon. In each of these streams more than one species of salmon may occur and in many three to five species do occur. Furthermore, in many streams more than one run of the principal species occur. Therefore, according to the biologists there are approximately ten thousand separate

U.S. Fish & Wildlife Service

Frequently salmon must battle through fast currents and over waterfalls to reach their spawning grounds. Here red salmon easily hurdle a six-foot waterfall near Brooks Lake on the Alaska Peninsula.

salmon spawning units and there must be a division of catch and escapement sufficient to sustain each unit.[6] This division can be achieved in a practical way only by defining major runs and learning the number of spawners needed on the spawning grounds for each. Accurate catch and escapement statistics as well as knowledge of how much gear and time is needed to catch the desired number of salmon are imperative in order to regulate the fishery precisely.

[6] For a good discussion of the biological implications see: William F. Royce, "Fishery Regulation in Alaska Salmon Management," *Fisheries Research Institute Circular No. 123* (Seattle: University of Washington, 1961), 6 pp.

Conservation of the salmon resource is further complicated in that the separate runs of salmon fluctuate in size owing to natural environmental conditions. An increase in water temperature may make an entire spawning area unsuitable. Since spawning is generally concentrated along the stream margins which dry up with any large drop in flow, droughts or other severe water shortages may cause the loss of large numbers of eggs. Floods may wash out the spawning beds. Landslides across a stream may partially or completely prevent salmon from reaching the spawning beds. Sea gulls, bear, beluga whale, trout, and the many other predators of salmon may become so active on a particular run as to materially reduce its size. Such natural ecological factors and relationships must be understood and taken into account.

Although biological research on the Pacific salmon has been carried on since commencement of commercial fishing in the latter part of the last century, much basic scientific knowledge necessary for proper management of the fishery is still lacking. A 1958 progress report by the Bureau of Commercial Fisheries of the U.S. Fish and Wildlife Service contained the following summation:

> The management of Alaska's commercial fisheries resources has long been the responsibility of the Federal Government. The objectives, of course, are the promulgation and execution of measures to achieve maximum sustained production of fisheries products. . . . One of the stumbling blocks today is the lack of knowledge of the fish themselves. What factors affect their reproduction and growth? Where and when do they migrate? To what natural fishing mortality are they subjected and how large a spawning stock is necessary to give maximum production? These factors vary from species to species and, with the species, from area to area.
>
> Therefore, considering the size of Alaska, its varied climate and geography, it is apparent that a great amount of basic information concerning the fish themselves must be obtained if proper management methods are to be developed.[7]

Some of the reasons behind this appalling condition will be discussed in later chapters. It is enough to emphasize here that an ingredient basic to a successful conservation program—accurate and useful scientific knowledge of the resource—is sadly deficient.

[7] U.S. Fish and Wildlife Service, Bureau of Commercial Fisheries, *Progress Report on Alaska Fisheries Management and Research, 1958,* Juneau, Alaska, November 1, 1958, p. 1.

In addition to these purely biological aspects, conservation of the resource is made even more complex and difficult through the social institution of a free and common fishery. Salmon along with most other fish in public waters are classified in the law as animals *ferae naturae*. Ownership while they are in a state of freedom is held by the government for the benefit of all, and no individual property rights can be claimed in the fish so long as they remain wild—unconfined and in a state of nature. Under this doctrine, fishing is considered a public right to be enjoyed by all. Hence, there is free access to the fishery, and private ownership in the resource can be established only after reducing it to possession through capture. For this reason fish are frequently referred to as a fugitive resource.[8] It is not possible in this study to go into the complicated legal history of this institution, but it should be mentioned that it derives from early English common law, that the Magna Charta is the basic document defining the right, and that it subsequently became part of the United States common law. Under court interpretation in the United States it has been determined that both the federal and state governments can grant exclusive rights to fish in public waters under their jurisdiction by enacting specific legislation, but in practice grants of this nature have been rare.[9] In the case of the Alaska salmon resource, with the exception of a few grants of exclusive fishing rights made to certain Indian groups, the doctrine of a common and free fishery has prevailed. The federal government did attempt at one time to abandon the doctrine in favor of creating exclusive fishing rights on a broad scale, but the controversial question was firmly settled by Congress in 1924 when an Act was passed explicitly providing that in Alaska "no exclusive or several right of fishery shall be granted therein."[10] Under statehood the doctrine has been positively reaffirmed in Article VIII of the state constitution which provides that "no exclusive right or special privilege of fishery shall be created or authorized in the natural waters of the State."[11]

In its simplest terms the problem created by the doctrine of a free and common fishery is that conservation can never become a

[8] Other natural resources included in this category are wildlife, migratory waterfowl, oil and natural gas, and ground water under certain conditions.

[9] For a review of the legal history of this doctrine see: *American Jurisprudence*, Vol. 22, pp. 666-708.

[10] 43 Stat. 465, Act of June 6, 1924, Section 1.

[11] *Constitution of the State of Alaska*, Art. VIII., Section 15.

practical economic objective for the individual. This is not the case with natural resources where rights in ownership are secure. Under private ownership the rational operator knows that if he is to maximize his returns from the resource over time he cannot act in an indiscriminate way in the present. If the operator can be shown that by proper conservation methods he can increase the yield from his resource in a way that is to his economic advantage, he will tend to adopt and follow such practices with little or no need for government regulation of his activities. The vast improvements that have been made in the last few decades by large timber companies in managing the lands and resources under their ownership provides a good example of what can be accomplished toward conservation under such conditions.

In the case of a common-property resource such as the fisheries, however, the individual operator is faced with an entirely different set of conditions. If the individual fisherman begins to realize that his actions along with the actions of others are depleting the resource, he personally is powerless to do anything about it. Even if he wants to pursue a policy of reasonable conservation by reducing his own fishing effort he can hardly be expected to do so as long as his competitors are still continuing their efforts. Far from preventing depletion of the resource, a policy of restraint pursued by the individual merely permits his competitors to take his place and catch a larger share of the legally free but practically limited resource. If his average yields begin to decline because of general overfishing, his only alternative if he wants to stay in business is to increase his own fishing intensity. If group action leads to extinction of the resource in a particular area, the individual can only hope there will be another area he can move to and begin the process again.

The population of most predators will begin to decrease as its actions reduce the population of the host species it is preying upon and thereby allow the host population to increase again. With man and fish under a common property arrangement no such ecological relationship holds. In a competitive economy with free entry into the fishery, the amount of fishing effort becomes a function of certain economic forces in the market and there is no guarantee whatever that intensity of exploitation of the free resource will subside as the fish population declines. On the contrary, as will be shown in

Chapter 3, economic conditions have been such that man's predation on salmon has tended to intensify as the population of the resource was depleted. In effect, the system of a free fishery allows and indeed induces man to become the most ruthless of all predators. Since his numbers cannot be controlled directly, the only alternative for the government has been to impose stringent regulations in an attempt to reduce man's efficiency more rapidly than his numbers increase.

2 *The Aboriginal Era*

Anthropologists are not certain of the origin of the aboriginal peoples who inhabit Alaska or how many different cultures may have preceded those that existed when the first Europeans came in the eighteenth century to explore the north and to exploit the rich natural resources. The fact is well substantiated, however, that the abundance of salmon along the coast from southeast Alaska to as far north as the Bering Sea was a significant environmental factor affecting their lives and cultural development. This was true not only of those who lived along the coast, for whom the sea was the main source of life, but also, to a lesser extent, of those in the interior who lived along the rivers which were the familiar highways for salmon on their annual migrations to the spawning grounds. Although the wealth of other marine and land resources cannot be minimized, where salmon abounded its influence upon the people was dominant.

It is not difficult to understand why the salmon resource was highly regarded. Measured by the caloric effort to obtain them, salmon have an exceptionally high degree of nutritional efficiency. Most of the food values are retained in the sun-dried or smoked state in which the native peoples generally preserved salmon, and in this form the product was easily packed, transported, and stored —to be drawn upon during the winter months when other food was scarce. Salmon prepared in this way was also a prime food for the sled dogs upon which many of these people relied for winter transportation.

Although the annual migrations of the salmon have their parallels among both land and marine animals and birds, the practical difficulties of taking full advantage of these migrations were considerably greater than with the anadromous salmon. In the case of mass movements of herds of land mammals, for instance, the hunters were seldom able to wait at a regular campsite for the arrival of the herd. Usually such a hunt involved an arduous pursuit. With the salmon, however, the regularity of the seasonal migrations and their concentration in confined sections of a river made the effort expended by the fishermen relatively low. In exchange for a few hours of heavy muscular effort, a single fisherman equipped with the simplest gear could land several thousand pounds of fish—considerably more than he could consume in a year. Compared with the weeks or months of heavy labor required by most primitive peoples to produce a year's food supply, salmon fishing was highly efficient.

The influence of salmon upon the native cultures along the coast came about primarily through the leisure time created. The short seasonal aspects of the salmon harvests made for periods of intensive activity, but since no effort had to be expended in laborious and time-consuming chores of sowing and cultivating in order to reap the annual harvests, lengthy periods of leisure time were created. This leisure was used by the natives to cultivate the arts, to elaborate on religious, social, and political concepts, and to perfect the material aspects of their culture. Consequently, where salmon were plentiful a unique and rich culture developed.

This cultural development has been an anomaly to many anthropologists. According to Philip Drucker,[1] development of high culture among primitive peoples is invariably linked with increased economic productivity that accompanies agricultural developments and the domestication of animals. Yet along the shore of northwest North America a complex culture developed without agriculture and possessing no domesticated animals other than the dog. Though Drucker does not subscribe to a theory of environmental determinism of culture, he believes the bounty of nature did permit a

[1] Philip Drucker, *Indians of the Northwest Coast* (New York: McGraw Hill Book Company, Inc., 1955), p. 1.

surplus of foodstuffs so great that a relatively dense population was able to enjoy an abundance of leisure. For various reasons yet unexplained, these peoples chose to devote that leisure to the improvement and elaboration of their cultural heritage.

Native reliance on salmon as a primary source of food varied considerably throughout Alaska, depending mainly on the availability of the resource in the various localities. One anthropologist, Dr. Gordon W. Hewes, has defined a "salmon area of the Pacific Coast" which extends from California north to the Bering Straits and includes many inland regions as well.[2] This salmon area is bound together by the extensive use of marine resources, with fishing for salmon the basic integrating factor. Dr. Hewes explains that sea fishing by the aboriginal peoples in the salmon area seldom extended as far out as the lucrative offshore fishing banks because adequate supplies of anadromous fish could be taken from the rivers and streams with greater ease. Hewes divides the salmon area into a number of subregions and he includes the coast of southeast and southwestern Alaska in what he describes as the "most highly developed aboriginal fishing complex on the continent" where salmon was everywhere the real staple.[3] Land animals were used only to a minor degree because the extreme density of the coastal rain forests reduced use of the hinterland to a minimum. It was in these two coastal regions that the highest cultural levels were attained.

In the subregions farther northward along the Alaska coast, salmon continued to be a primary ingredient in the diet of the people, though marine and land mammals and other fishery resources gradually assumed greater importance. Eskimos on the shores of Bristol Bay exploited the extremely heavy runs in the Nushagak, Kvichak, and Togiak rivers and although the surrounding tundra provided a few birds and land mammals, fishing for salmon remained the most important pursuit. In the Afognak-Kodiak region and along the Aleutian chain, salmon shared importance with various marine mammals as a primary source of food. In the interior of Alaska the Athabaskan Indians in the drainage basins of the Yukon and Kuskokwim rivers relied heavily for their sub-

---

[2] Gordon W. Hewes, "Aboriginal Use of Fishery Resources in Northwest North America" (unpublished Ph.D. dissertation, Department of Anthropology, University of California, 1957), p. 42.

[3] *Ibid.*, pp. 126-127.

sistence on a combination of salmon, whitefish, and various land mammals. These two rivers with their numerous tributaries provided an immense interior waterway for the migration of salmon from the Bering Sea, and salmon were an important food for the people and their dogs as far inland as the Klondike district in northwest Canada some fifteen hundred miles from the mouth of the Yukon. Fishing was the chief activity of the interior peoples during the summer months when the salmon migrations were under way, but unlike the situation farther south the supply of salmon put up in the summer was never large enough to carry families through the winter. Ice fishing along with winter hunting was a dire necessity. Northward from the mouths of the Yukon and Kuskokwim rivers the economy of the coastal Eskimos was based on a complex of fishing and mammal hunting with an increased reliance on sea mammals. Finally, around Bering Strait where salmon approach the vanishing point, fishing as a whole declined as an economic pursuit.

To determine the relative importance of the salmon fishery to the aboriginal peoples prior to European entry, Dr. Hewes prepared estimates of the annual consumption of salmon for the native groups in each of the major geographical regions. His calculations were based partly on estimates found in the journals and reports of the early explorers and partly on his own statistical computations which considered the size of the aboriginal population, their total caloric requirements, and the relative part of the total diet supplied by salmon. Table 1 (p. 18) is based almost wholly on these estimates.[4]

The figures show that an estimated 76,000 native people resided within the borders of the salmon area in Alaska, and they consumed an annual total of nearly 33.5 million pounds of salmon each year, or an average of 437 pounds per person per year. According to Hewes, it is unlikely that the total consumption fluctuated very greatly from year to year, since the total population was relatively stable for a long period preceding the ingress of Europeans. As would be expected, the highest per capita consumption (526 pounds) occurred in southeast Alaska, while the lowest was in the Aleutians (280 pounds).

By assuming that the estimated total consumption of 33.5 million

[4] *Ibid.*, pp. 226-227. (These figures also include salmon used for dog food.)

TABLE 1

ESTIMATED AVERAGE SALMON CONSUMPTION IN ALASKA BY MAJOR SUBREGIONS DURING THE ABORIGINAL ERA

Subregion	Estimated Population	Estimated Consumption in Pounds Per Year	
		Average Per Capita	Total
Southeast Alaska	9,500[a]	526	5,000,000
Central Alaska	12,500	487	6,090,000
Western Alaska	28,100	481	13,525,000
Interior Alaska	10,500	415	4,358,000
Aleutians	16,000	280	4,480,000
Total	76,600	437	33,453,000

[a] Total excludes small number of Haida Indians in the southern section.

pounds represents roughly the average annual catch of salmon, some significant comparisons can be made between catches during the aboriginal period and recent commercial catches.[5] In 1959 the total catch in Alaska amounted to about 147 million pounds of salmon or slightly over four times the average for the aboriginal period. This is of particular interest since it is frequently assumed that the salmon resource was in an undisturbed condition identical to the natural environment prior to the establishment of the commercial fishery. During the early period of exploration and settlement of Alaska, but prior to the beginning of commercial exploitation of the resource, there was a rapid decline in native populations owing to the swift spread of various infectious diseases, the destruction of food supplies, and other similar factors. Also, as the natives gradually came into the employ of commercial enterprisers they began to substitute processed foods for their usual native diet. According to Dr. Hewes, these influences materially reduced native catches of salmon during the period immediately preceding commercial development, and this reduction provided a biological "resting period" for the salmon.[6] This may help to explain the high

[5] Actually the aboriginal catch would be somewhat larger than this if spoilage, waste, and other similar factors were taken into account. Hence, the figure for the aboriginal catch is conservative.

[6] *Ibid.*, pp. 196-243.

productivity experienced on nearly every salmon stream at the beginning of the commercial era and the tendency to make the erroneous assumption about the virginal nature of the resource.

A variety of highly efficient fishing techniques were developed by the natives, and a surprising technological parallelism was exhibited in the fishing devices used by widely separate cultures. Even more surprising, however, is the fact that the basic fishing techniques used by the natives during this early period differed little from those employed later in the highly developed commercial salmon fishery. Advances have been made in fishing technology in modern times to be sure, but these belong to the accessory processes: in the application of power and other labor-saving devices for hauling and lifting, and for reeling lines and brailing nets; in transportation and navigation; in mass production of gear using refined materials; and in methods of processing and preserving fish. But few innovations have been made in basic catching techniques. Each of the major fishing devices now used—traps, seines, gillnets, and hooks—were employed to a varying extent during the aboriginal period.

The natives also used a number of other fishing devices such as weirs, harpoons, gaff hooks, dipnets, and bows and arrows, none of which is employed today. In most cases these devices were considered too efficient and were deliberately outlawed during the commercial era as a means of conservation. This brings to the fore a basic difference between the native and the modern fishery and pinpoints a major dilemma that arose with the beginning of commercial fishing and is still with us today—the relationship of gear efficiency to conservation. While the native peoples as a rule employed every possible efficiency in an effort to conserve their own energy in catching salmon, during the commercial era the realization that highly efficient gear in large numbers could be destructive to the resource led to the deliberate encouragement of inefficient methods of fishing as a means of conservation. For example, up until 1951 federal regulations allowed only sailboats to operate in the important Bristol Bay red salmon fishery. All power boats were excluded as a conservation measure. This attitude toward the relationship of fishing technique to productivity helps to explain why modern gear still basically resembles that of antiquity.

There is little evidence that the native attitude toward efficiency led to excessive exploitation or depletion of the stocks of salmon.

Two reasons help to explain this. First, among many of the native groups private ownership of the salmon resource through control of fishing rights was a highly developed social institution which served to reduce competition among tribes and tended to limit and stabilize the catches from any particular stream. The Tlingit Indians of southeast Alaska provide a good example. The region of the Tlingits was divided into fourteen loosely confederated territorial divisions or tribes and each of these was divided into a number of autonomous local lineages or clans which were formalized groups of relatives who traced descent to a common ancestor. Each clan retained possession of its lands and resources of economic importance and exploited them individually. The important fishing sites either were owned by individuals in the clan or were held in common by the kinship group to be used for the community good. Fishing rights were inherited by the descendants of the individuals or passed on to the group, and these rights were held to be inviolable. No Indian could fish in a stream owned by another except by invitation.

Dr. George W. Rogers presented a good analysis of this particular aboriginal institution in his recent study of southeast Alaska.[7] According to Rogers, the entire social organization of the aboriginal population might be described as a complex of interrelating mechanisms which worked together to maintain a fine balance between the population and the natural-resource base of the territory it occupied. He found that the system of strict clan control over resources was not so rigid as to preclude temporary arrangements which permitted the use by others of areas surplus to the needs of the clan. It was only necessary that application be made for such use and that a tribute in the form of a percentage of the harvest be paid to the clan owning the area. These and other means of interchange of area-use among the clans served to offset a poor harvest in any one section of the region. Rogers concluded:

> Looking at a generalized picture of aboriginal culture, then, one finds a close relationship between resources and population distribution and community organization, the territory determining the character and limits of the community. Within the framework of the tribe and its territories, a rhythm of seasonal activity was set in motion.

---

[7] George W. Rogers, *Alaska in Transition, The Southeast Region* (Baltimore: Johns Hopkins Press, 1960), pp. 272-280.

The whole system has not been described to suggest that a return to a primitive "golden age" would be desirable, but rather to demonstrate that within his own culture and utilizing the resources at hand, the Indian had managed to create institutions and organizations which permitted a sound and rational relationship of man to his environment and a balanced utilization of the natural resource base to support something far greater than a bare subsistence existence.[8]

While a return to the primitive golden age may be neither possible nor desirable, it is important to note that one of the basic problems of conserving the salmon resource during the commercial era stems from the common-property institution which was superimposed upon the resource with the coming of "civilization." Indeed, as will become apparent later, some of the recent and most constructive proposals for a more rational approach to the conservation of the resource amount to little more than a return to the aboriginal institution of private property and resource use-rights.

In addition to the aboriginal concept of property rights, the native attitude toward the resource itself helped to prevent depletion. Both Drucker and Hewes were doubtful whether these people understood the life cycle of the salmon, and they found little evidence that fishery conservation as we know it today was consciously practiced.[9] Nevertheless, salmon played an important part in mythology and ceremonial activities, and many of these peoples developed beliefs that were combined with ritual practices which assured the return of a portion of the salmon to the spawning grounds each year. For example, the Tlingit and Haida peoples believed that all living things—animals, birds, fish, and men—had a common origin and shared the world in a state of equality and mutual understanding. They believed that the salmon were a race of supernatural beings who went about in human form feasting and dancing beneath the sea. When the time came for the annual runs, these "Salmon People" assumed the form of fish and ascended the streams to sacrifice themselves for the benefit of mankind. The salmon migration was considered to be a voluntary act and it was thought that if human beings were careful not to offend their benefactors, the spirit of each fish would return to the sea, resume its original life and humanlike form, and prepare for the

---

[8] *Ibid.*, p. 278.
[9] Drucker, *op. cit.*, p. 138; and Hewes, *op. cit.*, pp. 21-22.

trip next season.[10] An elaborate First Salmon ceremony was held over the first catch from each important stream to honor and welcome the species, and many legends taught the young people that man was totally dependent on the good will of the Salmon People which they used for food, and therefore they must do nothing to harm or delay them. Whether or not there was a consciousness of the biological requirements of the species, such mythological beliefs and rituals provided an elemental ecological conception of the relationship of all living things which served to check man's misuse of the resource.

The aboriginal subsistence fishery, characterized by its stable and conservative use of the resource, gave way ignobly to the dynamic era of commercial exploitation which unleashed new economic and competitive motives under radically different social and political institutions. In the formulation of new policies for the development and conservation of the salmon resource, little thought was given to the well-being of the aboriginal population. There was an unbelievable abundance of salmon and millions of dollars to be made. Nothing else seemed relevant. The native people attempted to adjust as best they could, but the gulf between the new and the old order was too great and a general economic and cultural deterioration resulted as they lost control of their former natural-resource base.

---

[10] Drucker, *op. cit.*, pp. 140-41.

3 *The Commercial Era*

FROM THE TIME ALASKA was discovered by the Russian explorer Vitus Bering in 1741 until the late 1800s, salmon played only a minor role in the economic development of the region. The quest for furs was the dominant incentive for exploration and settlement. In their journals early explorers frequently noted the myriads of salmon found in the creeks and rivers along the coast of Alaska and alluded to their possible future commercial value, but it was over a century and a quarter, and after the rich natural bounty of fur-bearing animals had been exploited to a point near extinction, that economic conditions became favorable for large-scale commercial development of the salmon resource.

Probably the earliest fishing enterprise in Alaska was that organized by Grigorii Shelikov in 1785 at the Karluk River on Kodiak Island to provide dried salmon for the workers of his fur-trading concern. This and similar provisioning activities were typical of the slowly developing fishery of the ensuing seventy years. In the early 1800s, the Northwest Company posts began putting up small quantities of salmon for their own use and for sale to the trading vessels frequenting the coast. Salting of salmon for export on a small scale was under way as early as 1830, and Hubert Bancroft reported in his *History of Alaska* that officials of the Russian American Company each year shipped barrels of salted salmon to St. Petersburg as a delicacy to be enjoyed by their friends and relatives.[1]

Salmon fresh from the water is highly perishable and Alaska was isolated from the main food-consuming centers of the world. For those who began to see larger commercial possibilities in the vast hordes of salmon, the main problem was how to get the product to the distant markets at a cost competitive with other fishery products. Drying and salting as a means of preservation, while adequate for local provisioning, had commercial limitations. Both were slow, time-consuming processes and the final product was still subject to deterioration. What was needed was a simple process of preservation easily adapted to mass production and standardization which would assure preservation of the tasty, nutritional qualities of the salmon as found in the natural state. When a technique for preserving salmon in tin cans was developed in the 1860s, the potentialities of the industry began to be realized.

The first salmon cannery on the Pacific coast was established in California by the Hopgood, Hume Company in 1864.[2] Although the method first developed was extremely crude, the venture proved successful and within a few years salmon canneries were located all along the coast from California to Puget Sound in Washington. As the canning process improved and markets for the product expanded, the industry extended northward into Alaska where hundreds of productive salmon streams lay untapped. In 1878, eleven years after the United States purchased Alaska from Russia, the first two salmon canneries were established and successfully operated in southeast Alaska. The rush to establish other canneries began and the era of commercial exploitation of the salmon resource in Alaska was on.

Although salmon is still processed in a number of different ways, the canned product has been the most important in terms of both volume and value since the beginning of the industry. A study conducted in 1937[3] showed that an average of about three-quarters of

---

[1] Hubert H. Bancroft, *History of Alaska, 1730-1888* (New York: Antiquarian Press, Ltd., 1959), p. 661.

[2] John H. Cobb, *Pacific Salmon Fisheries,* Bureau of Fisheries Document No. 1092 (Washington: U.S. Government Printing Office, 1930), 295 pp. (This document contains a wealth of material on the early history of the fishery.)

[3] U.S. Tariff Commission, *Report to the United States Senate on Salmon and other Fish,* Report No. 121, 2nd Series (Washington: U.S. Government Printing Office, 1937), pp. 27-28.

all salmon caught was put into cans. Since that date increasing prices paid for canned salmon along with other factors have tended to shift an even larger proportion of the total catch into cans, and during the 1950s canned salmon averaged close to 90 per cent of the total Alaska catch. Table 2 shows the amount and value of the Alaska catch in the various forms in which it was processed in 1959.

TABLE 2

UTILIZATION OF ALASKA SALMON IN 1959
PRODUCTS AS PREPARED FOR MARKET

Salmon Product	Quantity (in pounds)	Per Cent of Total	Value (in dollars)	Per Cent of Total
Canned	85,357,872	86.54	$49,492,789	88.01
Frozen	9,053,325	9.18	3,581,237	6.37
Cured	4,203,502	4.26	3,155,994	5.61
Fresh	15,899	0.02	4,498	0.01
Total	98,630,598	100.00	$56,234,518	100.00

SOURCE: U.S. Department of the Interior, Fish and Wildlife Service, *Alaska Fisheries*, 1959, C.F.S. No. 2339, Annual Summary (Washington: U.S. Government Printing Office, 1960), pp. 5-6.

Because of the dominance of the canned product throughout the commercial era, this study will give primary emphasis to that segment of the fishery.

A number of physical and economic factors have been instrumental in shaping the basic industrial structure that emerged. The wide dispersion of the salmon fishing grounds along Alaska's lengthy coastline led to the building of many small processing plants. The perishability of the raw fish supply and the absence of cheap and effective refrigeration for long-distance hauling tended to fortify this basic structure. It has been only in recent years that improvements in transportation and refrigeration methods have begun to affect this pattern. Today canneries rely on a much larger area for their fish supply, and some fish are being frozen on the fishing grounds and transported out of Alaska to other canning centers on the West coast for final processing into cans.

In the early years, the isolation of many of the fishing areas and the primitiveness of Alaska with its sparse population necessitated the yearly importation of fishermen, cannery laborers, and supplies from the major population centers to the south. Consequently, from the beginning of the commercial era the main outfitting, employment, and financial centers for the Alaska salmon industry grew up outside the territory, primarily in San Francisco and Seattle. These cities also became the storage and marketing centers from which canned salmon was shipped by rail and water to domestic and foreign markets.

Headquarters for nearly all the canning companies operating in Alaska were also located at these centers. Thus, in time the Pacific coast became the base of the largest salmon industry in the world, with Alaska as the principal source of supply and Seattle and San Francisco as the primary organizing areas. In spite of the development and growth that has taken place in Alaska over the decades, this aspect of the fishery has remained relatively unchanged. While it is true that a much larger proportion of the fishermen and cannery workers are now local residents and more of the supplies are obtained locally, nevertheless the main center of decision-making for the Alaska salmon industry is still located outside the region. This pattern of economic absenteeism has given rise to numerous problems, conflicts, disagreements, and misunderstandings, which have greatly compounded the difficulties of conserving the resource.

By far the greatest portion of the salmon are caught within a two- or three-month season, and in some areas such as Bristol Bay the runs are cropped in a period of ten or twelve days. This seasonal characteristic has had a marked effect upon employment, capital needs, and the marketing system. It has led to high operating costs for the canners and placed a premium on accurate planning. Each year prior to the actual fishing season the cannery operator must forecast the probable size of the salmon runs and correlate his financial outlays with the estimated pack for each of his canneries. Nearly all his expenses including labor must be met before the season begins, and if the runs do not materialize or for some unforeseen reason the cannery is unable to put up the pack, he may sustain heavy financial losses. Once obligated to produce a certain size pack, the cannery operator is in no financial position to change his plans, and this has had a strong bearing on his attitude toward conservation regulations. While he may realize the need for conservation measures to preserve the supply, his attitudes and decisions are tremendously influenced by these immediate, practical business considerations.

In the early years of the industry, competition of the severest type developed among the growing number of cannery operators. Canneries were simple, inexpensive handicraft units offering an ideal activity for the enterprising individual of limited means who was willing to pioneer a new venture in a new territory. One company would prospect an area and establish a cannery near good fishing grounds. If the first one or two seasons proved financially successful other operators would rush in and establish their own canneries. With only a limited supply of fish available in a given area, a point was inevitably reached where increased fishing pressures began to reduce annual catches and profits per cannery. It was the logical outgrowth of a free fishery in a free competitive economy. Competition hinged upon the desire for both maximum cannery packs and elimination of rival concerns. The predicament in one area of Alaska was described in the following terms by a government agent in a report to Congress in the early 1890s:

> These corporations are rivals in the salmon canning business, and their rivalry is carried to such extremes that bloodshed at any moment will not surprise those who know the real conditions existing there. Now this bitter rivalry . . . if allowed to continue, will eventually destroy the salmon, for rather than allow company A to make a good haul of fish, company B will dam the stream and prevent the ascent of salmon, or company C will destroy the crop that would otherwise appear off the mouth of the stream four years hence; or A and B will join forces against C and actually destroy his nets and by force prevent his fishing.[4]

The situation was further aggravated by unstable market conditions. As new concerns rushed into the production of canned salmon the market was periodically glutted, which resulted in a corresponding lowering of the price. Mortality of companies, bankruptcies, and the abandonment of plants were high, but new concerns continued to enter into the little-understood operations, for it offered a gambler's chance for high profits. Sporadically a new company's

[4] U. S. Department of the Treasury, *Seal and Salmon Fisheries and General Resources of Alaska* (Washington: U.S. Government Printing Office, 1898), Vol. II, p. 405.

operation would return the entire investment with substantial profits in a single year.[5]

Out of these competitive conditions developed another basic characteristic of the Alaska salmon fishery—the strong tendency toward concentration of ownership and control of canneries in the hands of a few large corporations in an effort to rationalize production and marketing. The first step in this direction was taken in 1893 by dominant San Francisco interests, which led to the establishment of the Alaska Packers Association, one of the largest salmon-canning concerns in Alaska today. In 1894 the Association owned or controlled about 90 per cent of all canneries in Alaska with a pack equaling nearly 72 per cent of the total output.[6] By the turn of the century the corporation had come close to monopolizing the entire Alaska output of canned salmon. However, owing to the dynamic nature of growth within the industry during the next few decades the corporation was unable to retain its monopolistic position. Since that time new mergers and consolidations have taken place and there have been many company fights for dominance over specific fishing regions and species of salmon, but never again has a single firm been able to control the production and marketing of salmon as the Alaska Packers Association did during this early period. Instead there emerged a basic industrial structure consisting of a few large corporations, which controlled the greater part of the Alaska salmon pack, and a large but fluctuating number of small independent firms, many of which could only be classed as marginal producers.

It is difficult to quantify accurately the degree of concentration that has developed within the industry over time. However, a good general indicator is the distribution of the total pack by companies. In 1919 the Federal Trade Commission reported that five canning companies controlled over 53 per cent of the total Alaska pack.[7] An economic study of the industry published in 1939 showed that of 111 companies operating in Alaska and the Pacific Northwest in 1937, the nine largest concerns produced 58.3 per cent of the total

---

[5] Cobb, *op. cit.*, pp. 422-476.

[6] Gregory and Barnes, *op. cit.*, p. 93.

[7] U.S. Federal Trade Commission, *Report of the Federal Trade Commission on Canned Salmon*, Food Investigations, December 1918 (Washington: U.S. Government Printing Office, 1919), pp. 10-11.

American production of salmon. In addition, a number of these large producers marketed the output of the smaller concerns either on a commission basis or by outright purchase, and it was found that these nine leading firms actually controlled the marketing of nearly two-thirds of the entire American pack.[8] A review of the situation in 1959 shows that the six largest concerns owned over 40 per cent of the canneries and produced 53 per cent of the total Alaska output. On a regional basis, in western Alaska five operators out of a total of seventeen produced 70 per cent of the regional pack. In central Alaska five companies out of twenty-five produced 60 per cent of the regional output, and in southeast Alaska the five leading operators produced 54 per cent of the regional pack.[9] These figures do not show joint ownerships and other more complicated business interlinkages among the firms operating in Alaska, nor do they indicate the extent of control over marketing. However, they are sufficient to illustrate the oligopolistic nature of the Alaska salmon industry in which a few large firms dominate the industry through the production and marketing of a considerable percentage of the total output.

Another related characteristic of the Alaska salmon fishery is the degree of control the canning companies exercise over a third major segment of the industry—the fishing operations. Traditionally in the United States fishing has been characterized by the small independent fisherman who owns his boat and gear, and who chances the risks and physical hardships of the sea to bring in a catch which he sells as a free agent to the processors or distributors. In short, the fisherman generally has been an independent businessman in much the same manner as the small farmer. For various reasons, however, an altogether different pattern developed in Alaska. During the early years of the industry's development, Alaska's population was sparse and there were few qualified fishermen living in the territory. The seasonality of the industry made it uneconomic for fishermen to migrate north in great numbers to settle permanently in the remote fishing areas, and the distances involved were too great for the fisherman to travel back and forth each year in their own boats. Consequently, from the very beginning the

[8] Gregory and Barnes, *op. cit.*, pp. 105-106.

[9] Calculated from data provided in: *Pacific Fisherman*, January 1960 (Yearbook), pp. 59, 63, 67.

cannery operators undertook the organization and financing of fishing operations on a large scale in order to assure themselves an adequate supply of fish. This developed into a standard practice in which each spring the canners recruited large numbers of fishermen in San Francisco, Seattle, and other West coast cities, transported them to Alaska on company vessels, and paid them off at their home ports just as was done with the cannery laborers. It was costly to provide transportation, boats, gear, supplies, housing, and other necessities to maintain this pattern. Only the larger companies were able to finance these annual expeditions and by so doing they gained a large degree of control over fishing grounds in Alaska, especially in the more remote areas such as Bristol Bay.

As Alaska developed and more independent fishermen came to reside permanently in the territory, serious conflict arose between the resident and nonresident fishermen. In the earlier years this was primarily a conflict between the local independent fishermen and the nonresident cannery fishermen, but in later years a larger proportion of the nonresidents were also independent operators who came north each spring on their own boats, with their own gear, to fish the peaks of the salmon runs in the various districts and then return south in the fall. The political ramification of this resident–nonresident conflict will be considered in later chapters, but it is important here to note that the pattern of having company boats and gear operated by company-employed fishermen was difficult to alter, once it was established. Change was resisted not only by the larger canning companies who wished to maintain their advantage in controlling both supply and price, but also by the nonresident fishermen who had gained an economic foothold in the fishery, which they fought desperately to retain.

One of the best examples of the extent of this control occurred in the Bristol Bay area in western Alaska, one of the more remote fishing areas in the territory and also the greatest red salmon fishery in the world. Fishing was under such tight control by a few large corporations and the nonresident union that until the 1930s only a few residents were able to fish in the area even though they were willing to become company employees. This control was partially broken in the middle 1930s and more residents were employed by the companies, but up until as late as 1951 private ownership of fishing boats either by residents or nonresidents was practically nil in this most important of all fishing areas in Alaska.

The canning concerns exercised an even more direct influence over fishing operations through ownership and operation of the majority of traps, the most efficient form of gear in the salmon fishery. (See pages 43 to 47 for a description and illustration of each type of fishing gear.) In view of the labor-saving aspects of the trap and the pattern of ownership that evolved, it is not surprising that their use has been the subject of greater controversy than any other aspect of the fishery. Because of controversial aspects of the gear its use was outlawed in British Columbia, California, Oregon, and Washington; but in Alaska the federal government did not bow to the demands for abolishment and it was not until passage of the Alaska Statehood Act in 1958 that steps were taken to prohibit its use. Hence, throughout the entire period of federal management, traps have been in active operation in competition with the mobile forms of gear.

Figure 2 shows that from 75 to 90 per cent of all traps in the Alaska fishery have been owned and operated by the canning companies, and 30 to 45 per cent of all traps were concentrated in the hands of five leading companies. The significance of these figures is heightened when it is realized that traps accounted for well over 40 per cent of the total salmon catch in Alaska during this period.[10] Furthermore, traps have been used only to a limited extent in western Alaska where the majority of gear is already owned by the companies. In the two additional fishing regions where traps have been operated in competition with other forms of gear, they have at times taken as much as 75 per cent of the total catch. This has given the processing companies, especially the larger ones, an unusual degree of power at the extractive level, a condition seldom found in other major fisheries in the United States.

There are a number of reasons why this pattern of ownership developed and why the canners sought desperately to prevent traps from being outlawed. As mentioned previously, one of the key problems facing the individual canner was to obtain an adequate supply of fish at prices that would make the operation profitable. This problem was intensified by the marked tendency for a large number of concerns to enter the processing business. Competition among a growing number of firms for the limited resource eventually resulted in progressively lower average packs

[10] The percentage of salmon taken by the major forms of gear is discussed on p. 51 ff.

FIGURE 2. PATTERN OF TRAP OWNERSHIP IN ALASKA, 1915–1955[a]

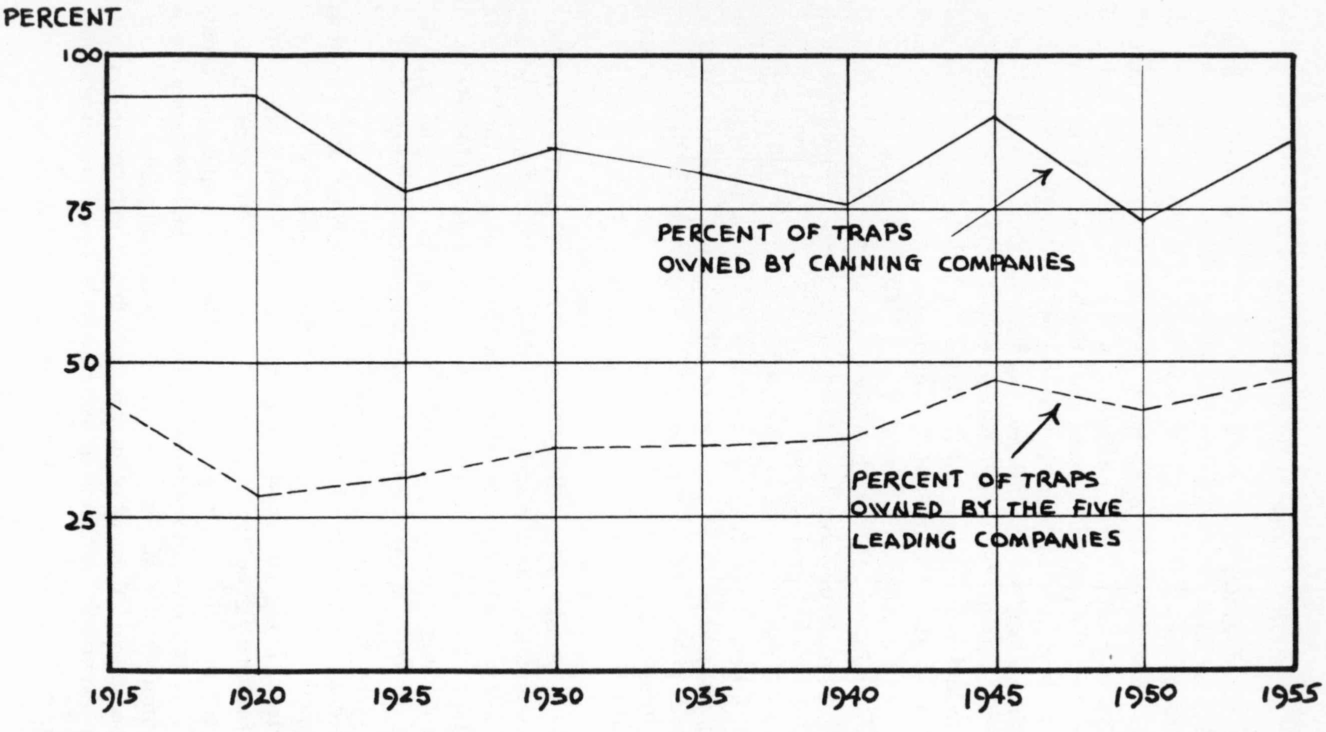

SOURCE: See Appendix A.

[a] Figures are based on five-year averages.

per cannery while at the same time the canners tended to bid up the price paid to the fishermen for the raw product. The individual cannery owner sought ways to overcome this insecure position by attempting to gain some degree of control over the limited supply, and company ownership of traps provided a logical means toward this end. This was made possible through the precedence that developed in which the first to establish a trap at a particular location gained use-priority of that site in succeeding years. Under this gentlemen's agreement no trap site could be lost except through failure to use it, and this gave a strong continuity to these possessory or "user" rights.

Throughout the history of the industry those who owned traps continually sought to have these user rights legally recognized so that locations could be acquired in fee simple. While they failed to accomplish this by legislation, the concept of user rights became so firmly established that it was possible for the companies effectively to own and control specific fishing locations in the waters of Alaska. These could be bought, sold, or traded with almost as much security and protection, for example, as a mining lease provides on the public domain.

Under these circumstances traps constructed and put into place provided a form of continuous fishing monopoly at that particular site. Mobile gear could not be set or drifted in the immediate environs and this physical feature was augmented by federal conservation regulations requiring that specific, sizable distances be maintained between all forms of gear.[11] By the judicious placement of a series of traps a canning concern could limit the effectiveness of all other fishing gear in a particular area. Entrances to bays, inlets, and estuaries could be blocked with traps in such a manner as to force the mobile gear to move from their usual lucrative positions near the mouths of the rivers and streams to the less productive areas in the open waters out beyond the trap locations where the salmon had not yet begun to congregate into definite

[11] These distances have varied over the years but in 1958 it was provided in the regulations that traps must be no less than 2,500 feet apart and that the distance between mobile units and traps must be no less than 600 feet. See: U.S. Department of the Interior, Fish and Wildlife Service, *Laws and Regulations for Protection of the Commercial Fisheries of Alaska, 1958*, Regulatory Announcement No. 56. (Washington: U.S. Government Printing Office, 1958), Section 109.25.

schools and runs. Thus, ownership of choice trap sites not only helped to assure a large and stable supply of fish for a particular company, but the traps themselves could be used as tools to force competing concerns out of business or otherwise to bring them into line. Further control was accomplished by bidding up the price of fish caught by the mobile gear on which these companies had to rely. Companies with traps were also in a superior position *vis-à-vis* the fishermen in the negotiation of raw fish prices. Since only the larger companies had the funds necessary to acquire the best sites and to pay the expenses of constructing the traps each year, they were in an advantageous position to effect a concentration of ownership. As the graph on page 32 shows, this is precisely the pattern that developed, and in this manner the most efficient form of gear—the fish trap—also became the most effective single element in controlling the supply of fish in Alaska.

Before turning to an analysis of the pattern of exploitation that emerged, it may be helpful to summarize some of the more important economic characteristics of the Alaska salmon industry. From its inception the industry has been developed almost entirely by absentee capital. It has been characterized by the cyclical presence of a large number of relatively small firms operating under highly competitive conditions. With the coming of large markets the small producers were outdistanced in a competitive race for dominance, and the balance of control went to a few of the larger packers. Many of these had financial interests outside the salmon-packing business, in lumber, logging, mining, shipping, and manufacturing industries along the Pacific coast. They were operators with substantial means who were able to expand their operations into several fishing regions simultaneously and thus spread part of their cannery risks. Many were able to finance their inventories over dull periods without the necessity of forced selling. The advantages of the larger producers were reflected, for example, in their ability to acquire superior cannery locations and in their acquisition of the best trap sites through purchase, lease, or original filing.

While this trend toward horizontal and vertical integration did not lead to a complete monopolization of the salmon fishery, it has made the position of the smaller operator precarious, often reducing him to dependence on can companies, brokers, and the larger packers, who in one way or another supply him with working capital and dispose of his product. For example, interviews conducted by Gregory and Barnes with the dominant packers revealed that they "implicitly allowed' a certain number of the smaller independent packers to continue operating for two reasons. The first was a business consideration—namely, that of passing the financial risk of packing the marginal output to the smaller firms. Also their packs aided in furnishing reserves, and, when sold, frequently earned a commission to the larger packer-broker. The second consideration was political—namely, "to keep the small operator in the field as a buffer between scheming politicians and the larger packers."[12] As will be seen in later chapters, the strong economic position of a few large absentee corporations afforded them a superior footing in the political process, both individually and through their various organizations and associations, and they played a dominant role in shaping the course of the government regulatory program to conserve the salmon resource.

The historical trend in the commercial exploitation of the Alaska salmon is revealed in Figure 3 (p. 36) which shows the total production of canned salmon from the inception of the industry until transfer of control over the resource from the federal government to the new-state of Alaska in 1960. From 1878 until the turn of the century production grew slowly. In the early 1900s the industry entered a period of dynamic growth as new markets were opened and great technological strides were made in fishing and canning techniques. The total packs increased at a rapid rate reaching a high in 1918 of over 6.5 million cases, whereupon a brief but severe decline set in until 1921 when the pack amounted to only a little over 2.5 million cases. This first major peak and decline resulted from the great demand created for salmon during the First World War and a demoralization of the markets which occurred immediately afterward. During the 1920s the pack of canned salmon began to increase again, but with wide fluctuations from year to year. The peak for the entire period of commercial exploitation was reached in 1936 when a total of 8.5 million cases were packed. Since then, except for a brief period during the Second World War, the trend in annual packs has been continuously and rapidly downward. In 1959, the last year of federal

[12] Gregory and Barnes, *op. cit.*, p. 141.

FIGURE 3. TOTAL PACK OF CANNED SALMON IN ALASKA, 1878–1959[a]
(*in millions of cases*)

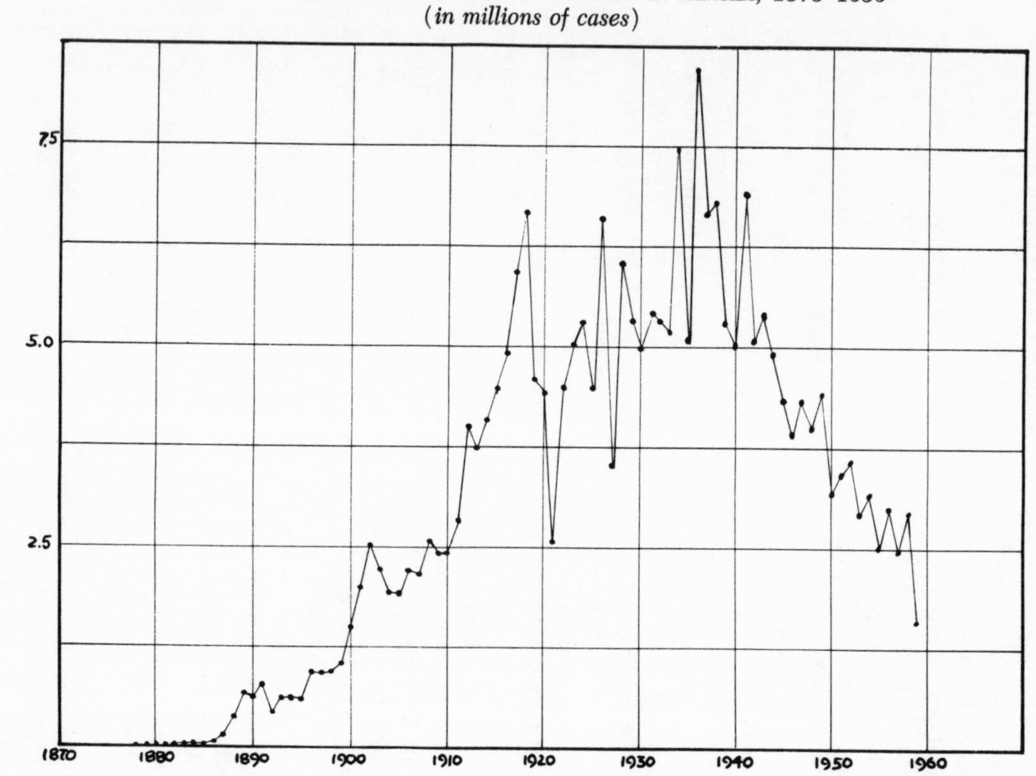

SOURCE: See Appendix A.

[a] Figures represent full cases of 48 pounds net.

management and control, the total pack amounted to only 1.6 million cases, the lowest pack since 1900 when the industry was in the early stages of development. It was over five times lower than the pack for the peak year of 1936.

Figure 4 compares the Alaska pack with production of canned salmon from all other North American salmon-producing areas combined, including British Columbia, Washington, Oregon, and

FIGURE 4. ALASKA CANNED SALMON PACK COMPARED WITH THE COMBINED PACKS FROM ALL OTHER NORTH AMERICAN AREAS, 1900–1959[a]
(*in millions of cases*)

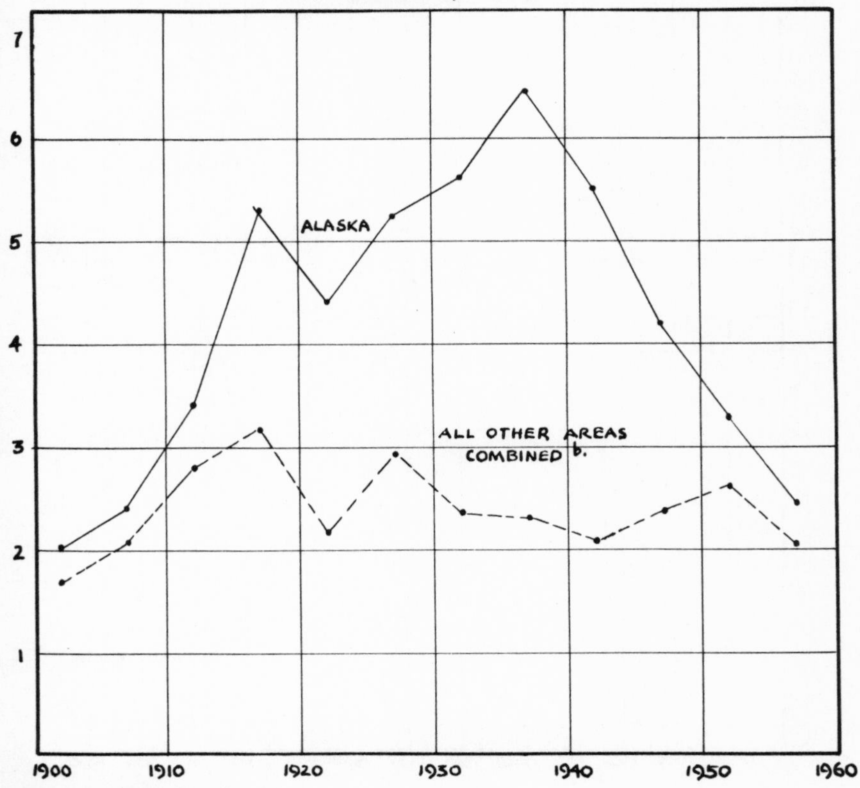

SOURCE: See Appendix A.

[a] Five-year averages.

[b] Includes British Columbia, Washington, Oregon, and California.

FIGURE 5. PACK OF CANNED SALMON FROM MAJOR PRODUCING AREAS ALONG NORTHWEST COAST, 1900–1959[a]

(*in millions of cases*)

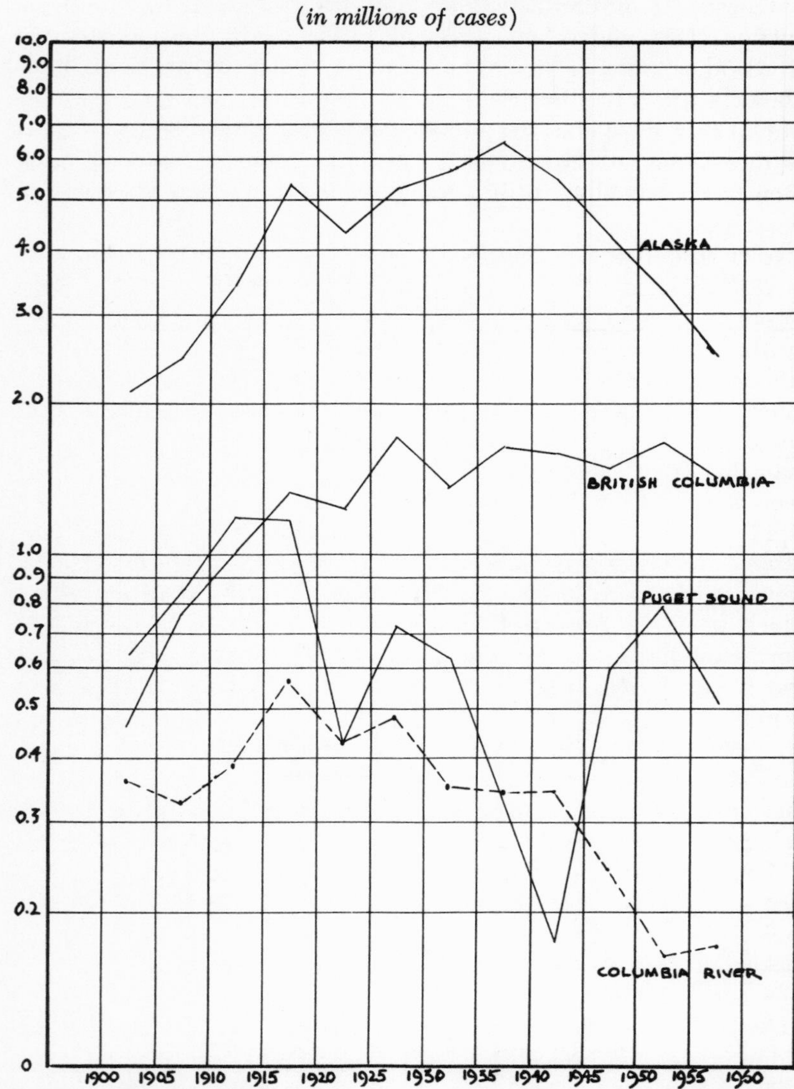

SOURCE: See Appendix A.

[a] Five-year averages.

California. Two important points are revealed. First, the total production of canned salmon from Alaska has greatly exceeded that of all other areas of North America combined. At one period the Alaska packs were nearly three times greater. Second, since the late 1930s the gap has rapidly closed, owing to the steady decline of the Alaska packs, while the combined packs from all other areas has remained relatively stable at around 2 to 2.5 million cases annually.

It is true that by combining the packs from all other areas, specific regional ups and downs have been concealed. The decline of salmon production along the West coast has not been limited to Alaska by any means. Figure 5 shows the production of canned salmon since 1900 from the major salmon-producing areas of North America. The pack from the Columbia River, once the most prolific salmon fishery in the world, has declined more rapidly and steadily than that from any of the other areas. The Puget Sound pack has been the most erratic. From 1915 until the mid-1940s it declined rapidly, but has shown a great improvement since then. The various developments such as industrialization, irrigation, hydropower generation, logging, water pollution, and urban expansion which have accompanied rapid population growth in the Pacific Northwest have taken a heavy toll of the salmon runs in these two regions. Salmon rehabilitation programs have only been able to minimize the adverse effects of this encroachment of civilization.

British Columbia is the one major salmon-producing area along the Pacific coast that presents a healthy pattern of production. The pack increased at a rapid rate until the mid-1920s and then stabilized at around 1.5 million cases. As the graph shows, the salmon packs for both Alaska and British Columbia followed almost identical trends until the mid-1920s, but the British Columbia pack leveled off and stabilized shortly thereafter, while the Alaska pack continued to climb to new heights before finally taking a steep downward tumble.

Clearly, the declining Alaska pack cannot be ascribed to any widespread natural phenomena, for such occurrences do not respect political boundaries. Nor is it possible to ascribe anything but a very minor part of this decline to the encroachments of civilization, for Alaska's settlement and development has progressed very slowly and most of the major salmon streams are still in relatively virgin condition. The answer must be elsewhere.

As mentioned earlier, there are thousands of salmon streams along Alaska's lengthy coastline and there are five distinct species of salmon. One of the most important underlying characteristics of the pattern of exploitation is the way in which the industry has shifted emphasis from species to species and from one fishing area to another over time with the result that the true condition of the resource at any given moment has been effectively con-

FIGURE 6. TEN-YEAR AVERAGE PACK OF CANNED SALMON IN ALASKA BY MAJOR SPECIES AND DISTRICT, 1900–1959
(*in millions of cases*)

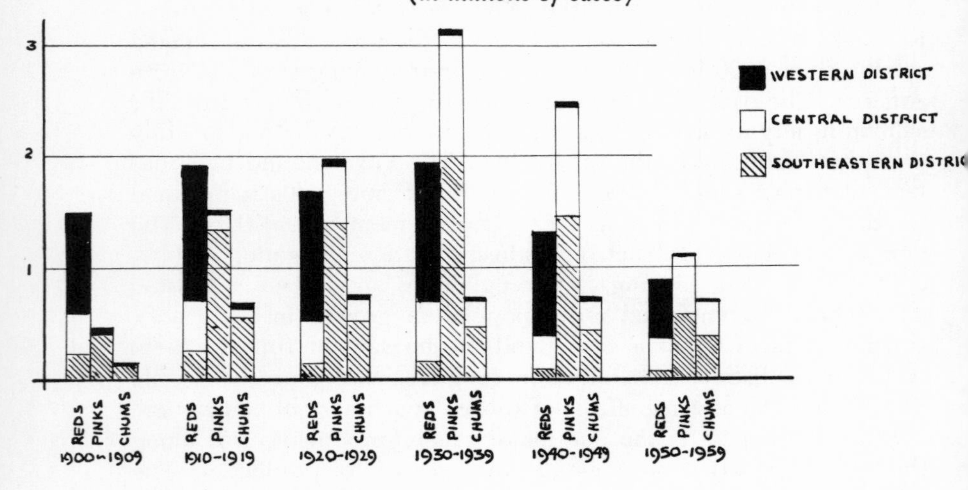

SOURCE: See Appendix A.

cealed. For the purposes of this analysis the fishing areas have been combined into three main fishing districts—western, central, and southeast Alaska—which are delineated on the map on page 2; and only the three major species of salmon—red, pink, and chum—are included.

Figure 6, based on ten-year averages, shows the changing composition of the total salmon pack in terms of the three major species and fishing districts from 1900 until 1959. During the first ten-year period, from 1900 to 1910, the higher-quality red salmon comprised nearly all of the total pack and these were caught and processed primarily in western Alaska. Production from the other two regions was negligible. During the three decades from 1910 to 1940, the size of the red salmon pack remained fairly stable, while pink and chum salmon came under heavy production, first in southeast and later in central Alaska. By the 1930s pink salmon accounted for well over half of the total Alaska output. During the last twenty years—the two decades of declining output—the red salmon pack from western Alaska and the pink pack from southeast Alaska showed the greatest decrease in total production. On the other hand, the chum salmon, the cheapest grade of canned salmon and the last to be exploited commercially, maintained a relative degree of stability.

In the last decade the average total pack was lower than it was in the first, and both the regional and species relationships were almost completely reversed. The once predominant red salmon from western Alaska accounted for only a small part of the total pack. Pink salmon was the predominant species and central Alaska the most important region in terms of total output.

A number of conclusions are apparent from the changing regional–species composition of the salmon pack. During the early years when the industry was developing at a rapid rate the supply of fish presented no obstacle to expansion. Only the most productive areas and the species of highest quality were being exploited. Lack of markets was the main limiting factor. As depletion occurred in a particular area the industry was able to expand into other regions and to the production of the lower-grade species as market conditions warranted. As a result, the total output continued to rise. From the 1920s onward, the physical limitations of supply became a factor of growing importance. By this time markets were well established. All species were being exploited heavily, but there were fewer and fewer opportunities to offset depletion by expanding operations into new fishing areas. The trend in the total pack continued upward, but the rate of growth was decreasing and there were extreme oscillations in the pattern of output as a result of heavy fishing pressures. After the peak packs in the 1930s, there was a continuous decrease in the supply of fish in every region of Alaska and, as will be shown later, fishing pressures continued to increase as the output steadily declined. This pattern of production tended to mask the seriousness of depletion in specific instances, especially during the period when the total pack of canned salmon was increasing. By the time the total pack began to waiver and to show definite signs of decline, the resource had already been seriously depleted in many areas; some of the major salmon-producing streams had been all but wiped out.

The number of salmon canneries operating in Alaska each year since the beginning of the industry is shown in Figure 7. The changing relationships in the number of canneries operating in each of the fishing districts provides further evidence of the scouring process described above. In the early 1900s the largest number of canneries was located in the western district where twenty-five to thirty plants were operating. As pink salmon came under ex-

FIGURE 7. NUMBER OF SALMON CANNERY PLANTS OPERATING IN ALASKA, TOTAL AND BY REGION, 1878–1959

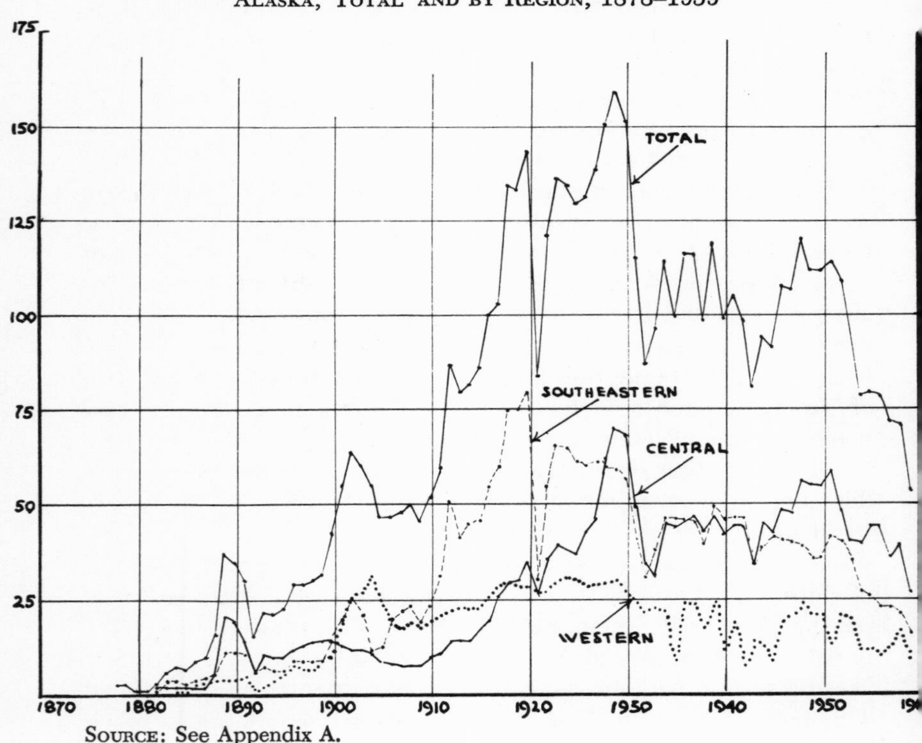

SOURCE: See Appendix A.

ploitation, the number of canneries began to grow in southeast Alaska, reaching a peak of about eighty plants during the First World War. The peak in central Alaska came in the late 1920s when sixty-five to seventy canneries were operating in that region. By the late 1950s, there were around thirty canneries operating in central Alaska, about twenty in southeast Alaska, and less than fifteen in western Alaska.

From 1878 until around 1920 there was a close relationship between the total number of canneries and the total pack of canned salmon. Both were expanding rapidly at about the same rate. The three major dips in the number of canneries during this early period represent attempts within the industry to reduce production through concentration and consolidation of operations, and these dips are reflected in the total pack.

From 1920 onward, there have been some basic differences in the two patterns. Canneries reached an apex in the late 1920s when the country was enjoying a period of great industrial prosperity. In the summer of 1929, just before the financial crash, the number of canneries stood at an all-time high of 160 plants. The number was greatly reduced during the depression even though the total salmon pack was still rising. There was a further decrease in the number of operating canneries during the Second World War when many operations were temporarily consolidated as part of the war effort, but during the booming postwar years a significant increase in the number of plants occurred even though the total pack was well along on its downward trend and the resource itself was obviously in an advanced state of depletion. No great reduction in the total number of canneries took place until around 1952.

Throughout the commercial era four major types of fishing apparatus have accounted for the catch—gillnets, purse seines, trollers, and traps. The trends in fishing effort and the changing relationships among the various forms of gear are key factors in understanding the pattern of exploitation. Brief descriptions of the gear, which are illustrated in Figure 8, are presented here.

The oldest form of fishing gear on the Pacific coast is the gillnet. These nets are generally operated from cabin power boats about thirty feet long with power-driven drums to haul in the nets. In a few areas the nets are also staked or anchored to the

FIGURE 8. MAJOR TYPES OF FISHING GEAR

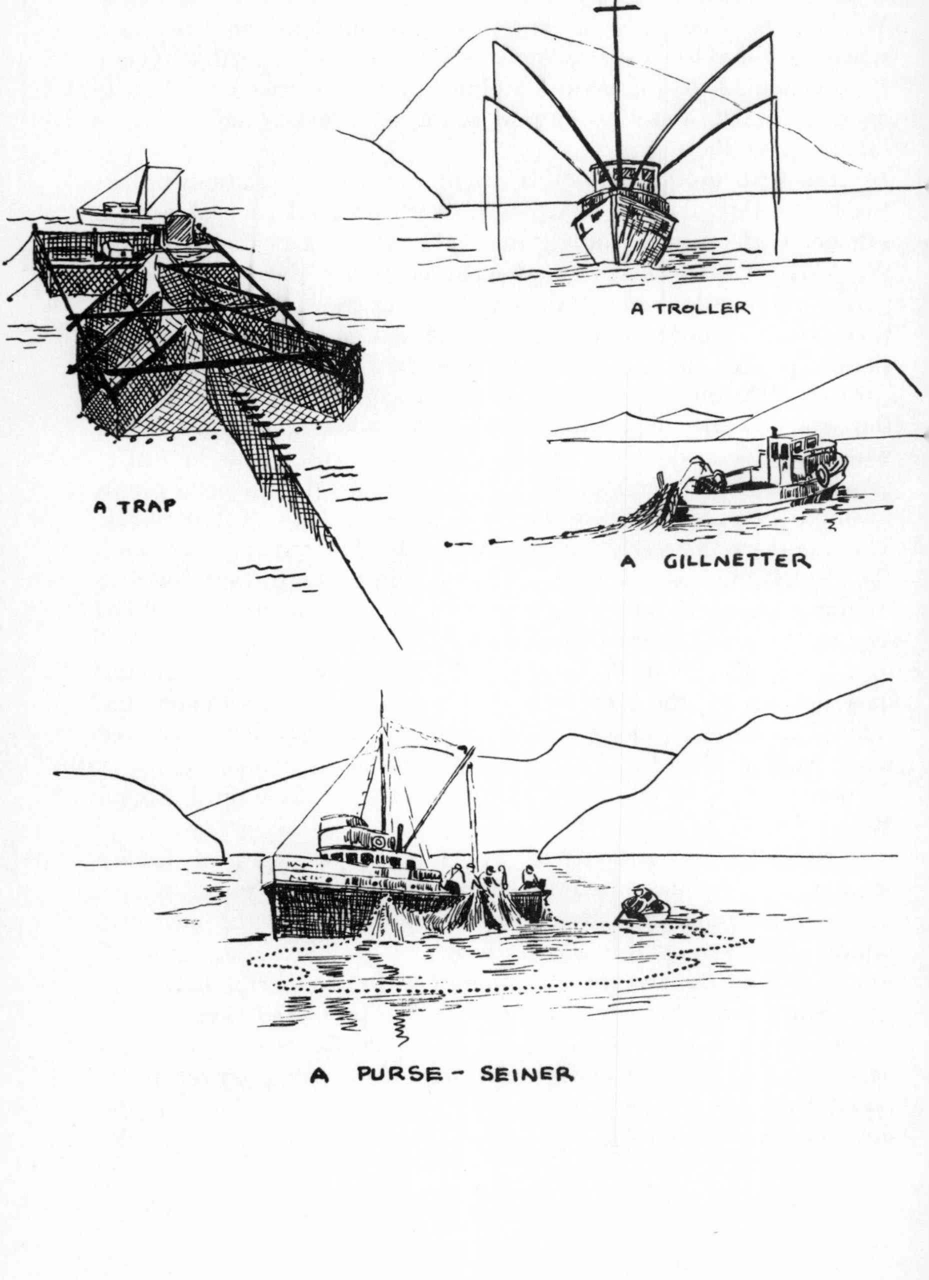

A TROLLER

A TRAP

A GILLNETTER

A PURSE-SEINER

shore. The net, which is hung from a cork line at the surface, has sinkers attached to the bottom so it will stand erect in the water. The length, depth, and size of mesh depend upon the area, the size of fish to be caught, and government regulations. Gillnets are used principally in and around the mouths of the larger rivers. They are much more effective in muddy or silty water or at night when the mesh is not visible to the salmon. The net is played out in a straight line from the stern of the boat. The fisherman drifts the boat and gear across or through a known fish run, and when a salmon runs into the net its head and gills become entangled in the mesh. Periodically the fisherman reels in the net on the power drum and removes the catch. Usually the boats are operated by one or two men. The relatively inexpensive nature of this gear has made it particularly appealing to the individual with limited capital.

Purse seines have also been employed since the early years. Their use increased enormously around the turn of the century following the introduction of power boats, which greatly improved their mobility and effectiveness. The purse seine is a net of heavy twine supported on the surface of the water by corks. The bottom of the seine is heavily leaded and has a draw rope running through it. When a school of fish is sighted the net is payed out around the school. The draw line is tightened to close the bottom of the net in the manner of old-fashioned purse strings. The seine is drawn in until the salmon are enclosed in a narrow circle alongside the boat where they are brailed into the hold with a dip net. In recent years power blocks, winches, and other similar devices mounted on the boats have made the seine boats more efficient. The boats have also increased in size over the years, but in Alaska the over-all length has been limited by government regulation to fifty feet as a conservation measure. The boats carry a crew of around seven men and they can operate either in the protected waters along the coast or far out at sea. In a few areas where there are beaches, sand bars, or gravel spits, the seines are operated from the land.

The third type of salmon-fishing gear is the trap. It was first developed in the state of Washington in the 1890s and was introduced into Alaska around the turn of the century. The high efficiency of the trap led to its rapid acceptance throughout the

U.S. Fish & Wildlife Service

This efficient salmon fishing trap, built of log piles and wire netting, extends out from the shore for a half mile or more across the travel routes of the homeward-bound salmon.

territory except in Bristol Bay and a few other areas where physical conditions made its use impractical. The trap is a huge permanent installation of log piles and wire netting that extends out from the shore for about a half mile across the path the salmon travel as they wend their way toward the rivers and streams. Salmon follow much the same travel routes from year to year, and the traps are located to take maximum advantage of this fact. As the salmon move along the shore they strike a barrier of netting which guides them into the trap. They pass through a series of V-shaped openings of webbing until they reach the pot from which they cannot find their way out. From the pot the salmon are allowed to pass through a small tunnel into the spiller where they can be brailed into a scow alongside. Traps may be either pile driven or floating, the latter being more common. They are nearly always removed each fall and reconstructed again at the same site at the opening of the next season. Usually a single watchman is hired to live on each trap during the season to check on maintenance needs and to prevent the pilfering of fish. The annual costs of construction are high, but operating costs are small in relation to the efficiency of the traps.

The fourth type of commercial fishing gear is the troller, which uses the simple hook and line. Troll boats average forty feet in length and are generally built to ride an open-ocean storm. They carry ice in the holds to allow for a week or more of fishing at sea. Two trolling poles rise high above the mast and two more lie back from the bow. When the boat is fishing, these poles are dropped outward, carrying stainless-steel lines that are stretched almost straight down for thirty fathoms or more by heavy lead weights. Each line may carry as many as seven leaders with hooks, lures, and bait. The boats move along under power at two or three knots while fishing. Usually there is only one man per boat. Little change has taken place in troll gear from early times, but there has been some increase in productivity through use of larger and faster power boats. Trolling is limited to two species of salmon—king and coho—the only species that will regularly strike at lures. The troll-caught salmon are nearly always processed as fresh or frozen rather than canned, and the percentage of fish taken by trolling is minor in comparison to the catches of the other forms of gear. For these reasons, trolling gear is not included in the following analysis.

Figure 9 shows the total number of gillnet boats, seine boats, and traps in the Alaska salmon fishery from the turn of the century until 1959. Use of the three forms of gear increased markedly during the early period when the industry was growing rapidly. Traps enjoyed the greatest rate of increase, rising from around 60 in 1906 to well over 600 in 1920. During the same period seines increased from around 200 to 800, while gillnet boats increased

FIGURE 9. NUMBER OF UNITS OF GEAR BY MAJOR TYPE OF GEAR, 1906–1959

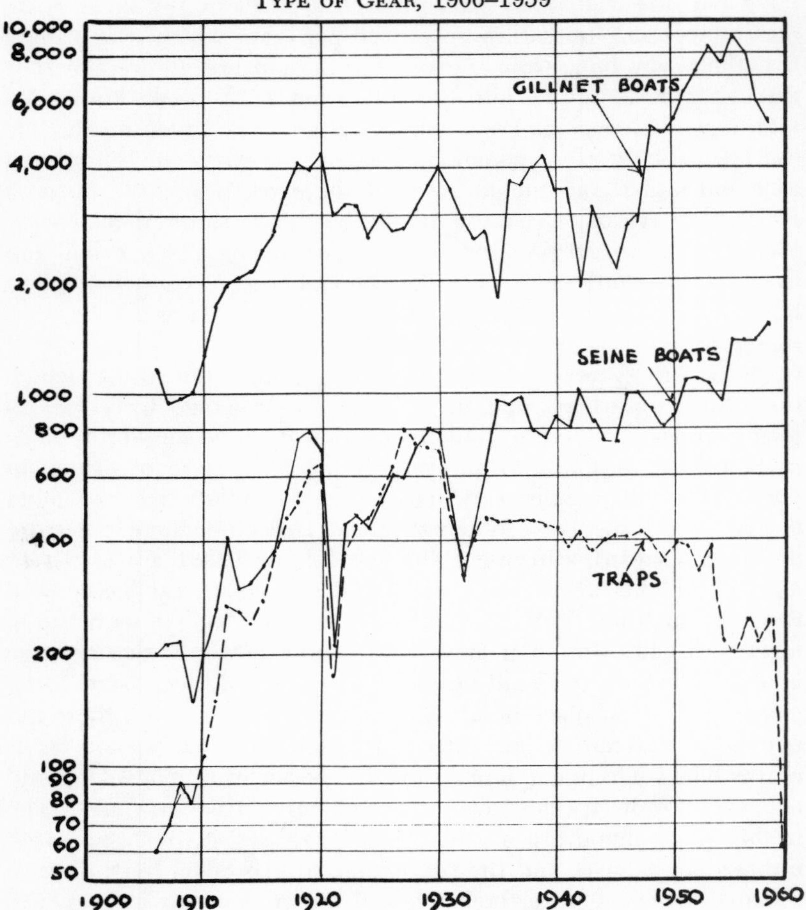

SOURCE: See Appendix A.

from approximately 1,000 to 5,000 boats. This represents an increase of about 900 per cent for traps, 300 per cent for seines, and 400 per cent for gillnets. During the same period the total production of canned salmon increased by only 225 per cent. The number of units of gear decreased tremendously during the early 1920s when markets for salmon were depressed, but began to rise again as markets revived. With the coming of the Great Depression, traps were reduced from an all-time high of 799 units in the late 1920s to about 400 units, a level at which they remained until the 1950s. In the next few chapters details of the federal conservation program will be set forth; here it is important to mention that this abrupt decrease in the number of traps was primarily the result of government policy. What is important for the present analysis is that this reduction in traps was followed by a sudden increase in the number of mobile units of gear. The effect of the trap reduction was not to reduce over-all fishing effort, which was the desired objective, but to shift part of the trap catch to the purse seines and gillnets.

An astonishing fact is the tremendous influx of mobile gear that occurred during the 1940s and 1950s when the output of the industry was fast decreasing. As may be recalled, in 1936 total production of canned salmon reached a peak of a little over 8 million cases and then began a rapid decline, reaching a low of 1.6 million cases in 1959, a decrease in production of over 80 per cent. Yet as the graph shows, in spite of this great decline in output the number of units of mobile gear continued to rise. The number of gillnet boats increased from an average of 3,000 units in the late 1930s to 7,500 units in the late 1950s, an increase of approximately 150 per cent. The only significant deviation in this upward trend occurred during the Second World War when manpower was short. Purse seines followed the same trend, rising from about 700 units in the late 1930s to over 1,500 units in the 1950s, an over-all increase of approximately 115 per cent. Since traps remained at a stable level during 1940s and 1950s, this continued increase in mobile gear cannot be attributed to a decrease in the number of traps, as was the case in the early 1930s.

Equally revealing is the trend in the average catch per unit of gear from 1906 to 1959, which is shown in Figure 10. Traps have enjoyed the highest average catch per unit, followed closely by seines, with gillnets last at a considerably lower level of effectiveness. The general downward trend in average catches for all three types of gear throughout the entire period is most significant. In the 1900s the average catch per trap amounted to over 100,000 fish, but by the 1950s this had decreased to less than 50,000 fish per trap. Seines showed a greater rate of decline in average catches,

FIGURE 10. AVERAGE CATCH PER UNIT OF GEAR FOR EACH MAJOR TYPE OF GEAR, 1906–1959[a]
(*in numbers of fish*)

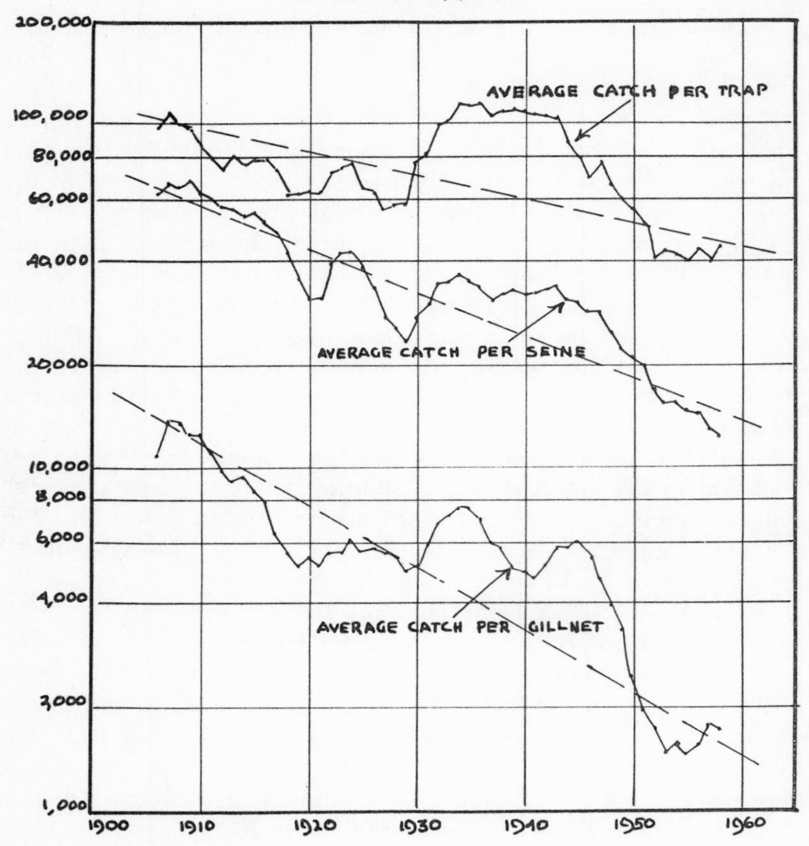

SOURCE: See Appendix A.

[a] Five-year moving average.

falling from nearly 70,000 to about 15,000 fish per unit. The rate of decline for gillnets was even greater, falling from about 15,000 to 1,500 fish per boat. Thus by the 1950s the average catch per unit of gear had decreased by about 50 per cent for traps, 80 per cent for seines, and 90 per cent for gillnets.

The declines in catch per unit occurred even though technological improvements greatly increased the productive potential of each unit. Shortly after the turn of the century the mechanical revolution invaded the salmon fishery. Gasoline and diesel engines were installed in the growing fleet of fishing boats and this increased their maneuverability and effectiveness. The floating trap represented an important improvement over the older pile-driven type and it was rapidly perfected and put into use. New inventions such as radio, radar, sonar, power winches, power blocks, better and stronger nets, and many other innovations were adopted over the years with a view to increasing the efficiency of gear; and yet the general trend in catch per unit has been downward. Few industries can exhibit a continuous decrease in unit productivity in the face of great technological strides.

Around 1930 there was a significant increase in the unit productivity of each type of gear, which lasted for a period of about five years, before the decreasing trends set in again. This major hump was primarily the result of the large reduction in the number of traps which occurred at that time. The average catch of the remaining traps increased from around 60,000 to a little over 120,000 fish, or over 100 per cent. Obviously only the least productive traps were closed, and the value and productivity of those remaining in operation was greatly increased.[13] The reduction in the number of traps also resulted in an increase in the average catches of the seines and gillnets by around 50 per cent each. These higher average catches for each type of gear began to decrease as more mobile gear entered the fishery, and by the 1940s the downward trend in unit productivity was again well established. This provides evidence of the futility in a free fishery of attempts to reduce fishing pressures through measures affecting only one type of fishing gear.

The percentage of salmon taken by each major form of gear from 1906 to 1958 is shown in Figure 11. The figure illustrates the interchangeability which exists among the three types of gear. In the early years seines and gillnets accounted for well over 75 per cent of the total salmon catch. As all types of gear increased rapidly in numbers during the ensuing years, traps began to ac-

---

[13] Many of the traps given up by the canning companies were so-called "dummy traps" which were put into place each year primarily to prevent another company from establishing a trap at that location. They were valued as a protective device and were not fished intensively.

count for an increasingly larger percentage of the catch. The seine gear was pinched the hardest. By the late 1920s, traps had reached a peak in numbers and they accounted for over 50 per cent of the total catch, while seines accounted for only about 25 per cent and gillnets around 20 per cent. With the reduction in the number of traps in the early 1930s, the percentage of salmon caught by seines and gillnets began to increase. By the late 1950s the share of salmon taken by each form of gear had reverted to

FIGURE 11. PER CENT OF SALMON TAKEN BY EACH MAJOR FORM OF GEAR, 1906–1958[a]

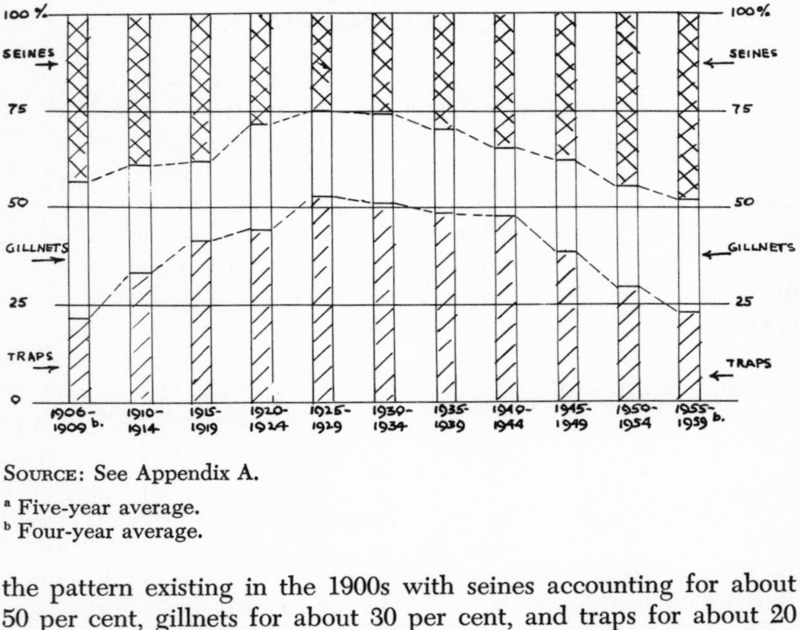

SOURCE: See Appendix A.

[a] Five-year average.

[b] Four-year average.

the pattern existing in the 1900s with seines accounting for about 50 per cent, gillnets for about 30 per cent, and traps for about 20 per cent of the total catch. Gillnets have maintained a greater stability in percentage of catch throughout the entire period, while traps and seines appear to have been the most competitive.

Figure 12 shows the number of fishermen, the number of shore employees, and total employment in the Alaska salmon fishery from 1906 to 1958. The most significant feature is the continuous upward trend in the number of fishermen. Early in the century there were approximately 3,000 fishermen in the industry while in the late 1950s there were well over 12,000 fishermen. Since the late 1930s, the number of fishermen has nearly doubled, from 6,000 to 12,000, even though the total catch was rapidly declining.

The trend in the number of cannery workers and other shore employees has not followed this same pattern. There was a rapid increase in this class of employment until about 1920 when nearly

FIGURE 12. EMPLOYMENT IN THE ALASKA SALMON INDUSTRY, 1906–1958

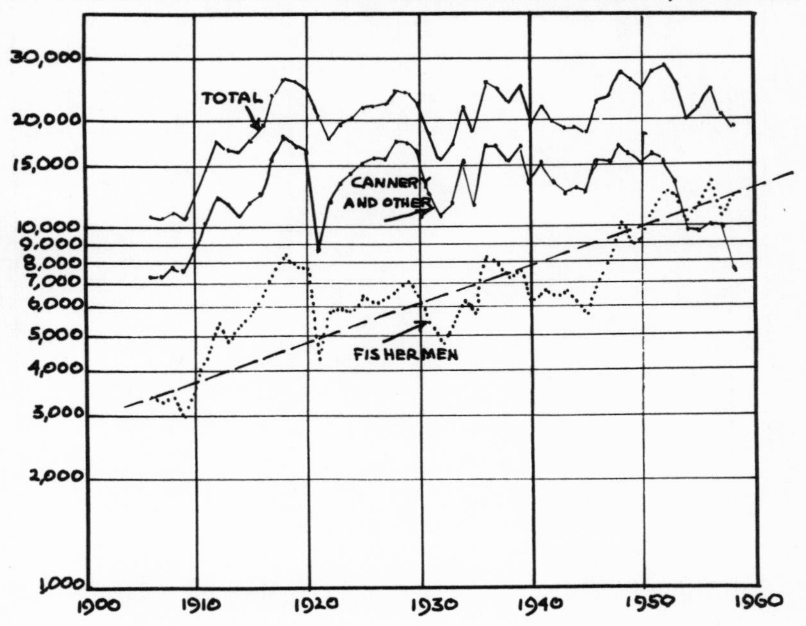

SOURCE: See Appendix A.

18,000 were employed. Since then cannery and shore employment has fluctuated in relation to the number of processing plants in operation, but on the whole averaged around 15,000 until 1950. During the 1950s shore employment decreased to around 8,000 in 1958, or approximately the same number that was employed in the early 1900s.

It is of special importance to note that in 1954 the number of fishermen exceeded the number of cannery and other shore workers

FIGURE 13. TOTAL NUMBER OF FISHERMEN AND AVERAGE CATCH, 1906–1958

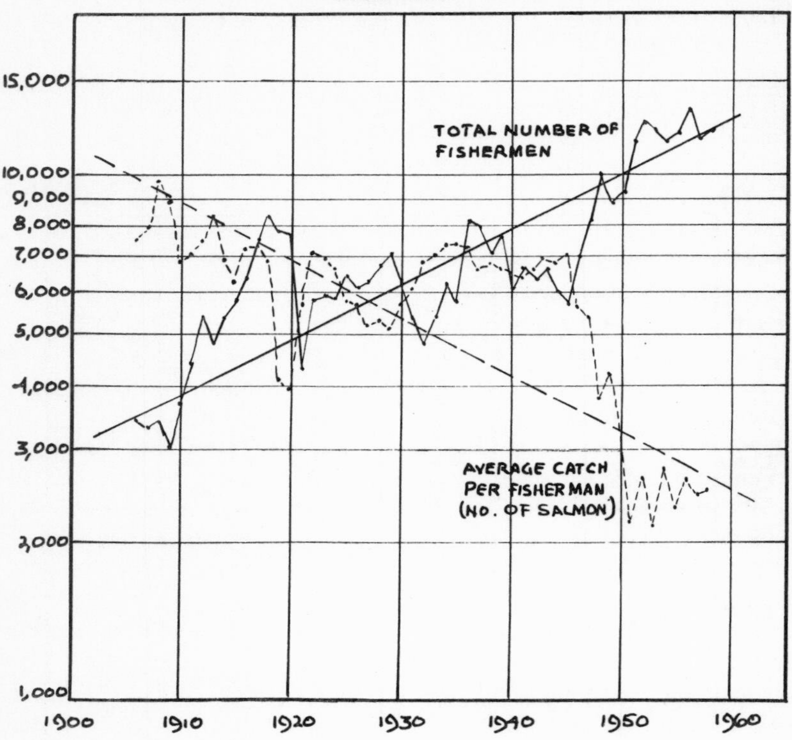

SOURCE: See Appendix A.

for the first time since commerical exploitation began. Throughout most of the history there has been about one fisherman for every two shore workers, but by 1958 there were three fishermen for every two shore workers. These shifting trends have resulted in a relatively stable total employment in the industry since 1920, at around 22,000 to 24,000 persons.

A comparison of the number of fishermen and their average catch of fish since 1906 is shown in Figure 13. At the beginning of the century each fisherman caught about 9,000 fish per year, but by the 1950s the average catch was around 2,500 fish, a reduction of more than one-third in average productivity. This decreasing trend in average catch per fisherman is almost the direct inverse of the increasing trend in the total number of fishermen throughout the entire period. The major fluctuations in the average catch per fisherman are nearly identical to those noted in the discussion on efficiency of the mobile gear units. When the number of traps was curtailed around 1930, there was a sizable increase in the average catch for all remaining gear units. The beneficial effect this had in improving the average catch per fisherman is well illustrated in the graph, but the combined forces of a decreasing supply and an increasing number of fishermen eventually turned the trend in average catches downward again at an ever increasing rate. There has been a slight increase in the average catch per fisherman since about 1950, a result of further decreases in the number of traps.

As the graph clearly shows, more and more fishermen have been induced into the fishery while the average productivity of each has steadily declined. By the late 1950s salmon packs had decreased to about the size they were in the early 1900s when the industry was in its infancy, and yet there were four times more fishermen and each was catching less than one-third the number of fish.

To understand this apparent violation of normal business practice and good common sense, it is necessary to look at the trend in prices and value of canned salmon. Figure 14 shows the trend in the real wholesale price per case of canned salmon for each of the three principal species from 1913 to 1957. These real prices have been corrected to remove the general inflationary trend in the value of the dollar in order to show the true value of salmon in relation to the value of all other commodities. This means that any variation in the real prices must be attributed to factors other than the fluctuations in the value of money.

The price of each of the three species of canned salmon has shown a significant upward trend throughout the entire period. The higher quality, higher priced red salmon has shown a constant upward trend from around $10.00 per case in 1913 to a little over $30.00 in 1957, the only major deviations being the exceptionally high prices during the period of prosperity in the 1920s and the corresponding slump in market price during the depression in the 1930s. With this one exception, the price of red salmon has shown no sign of weakening even at the extremely high prices in the late 1950s. The real prices of pink and chum salmon have been much less

FIGURE 14. REAL PRICE PER CASE OF CANNED SALMON, 1913–1957[a]

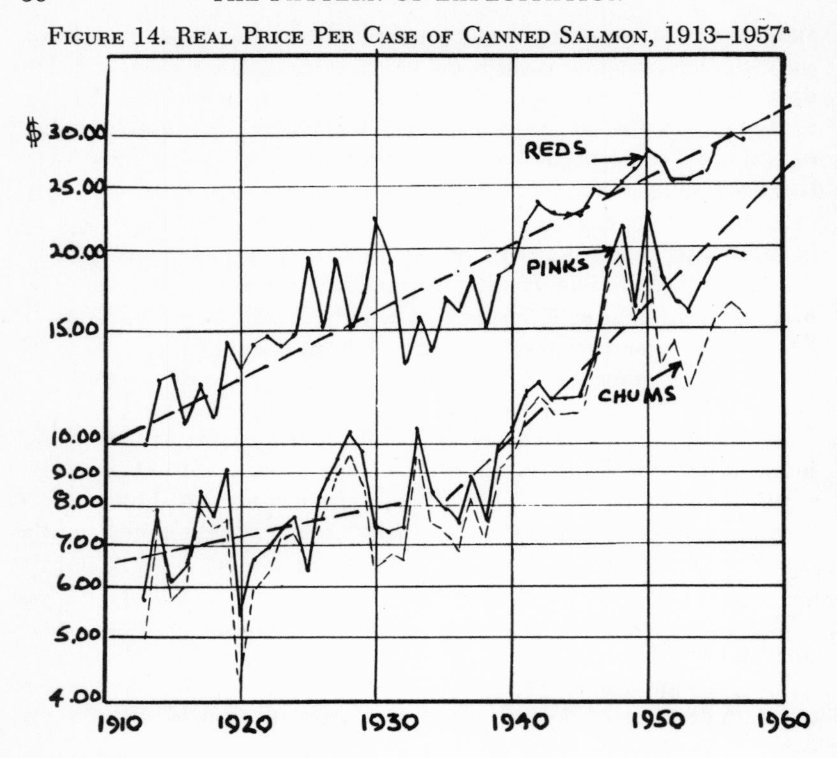

SOURCE: See Appendix A.

[a] Prices corrected to remove changes in the value of the dollar. (W.P.I., 1947–1949=100)

stable, but they generally show a gradual increase from around $6.50 a case in the early 1900s to around $8.00 a case in the mid-1930s and then a very rapid increase to around $18.00 per case in the early 1950s. Since then both species have shown a marked weakness in price as compared to reds, with chums showing a greater weakness than pinks.

Figure 15 shows the general trend in the wholesale value of canned salmon in relation to the quantity produced. The trend lines are freehand curves based on five-year averages. Until the 1930s the constant trend in both supply and price was upward, and this resulted in the rapid increase in the wholesale value of canned salmon. Beginning in the late 1930s, production decreased steadily as a result of depletion, but prices for all species of salmon continued upward at a rate sufficient to maintain an upward trend in the total value of the product until the early 1950s. Since then the slackening in the price of chum and pink salmon coupled with

FIGURE 15. TRENDS IN THE PRODUCTION AND WHOLESALE VALUE OF CANNED SALMON COMPARED, 1905–1959[a]

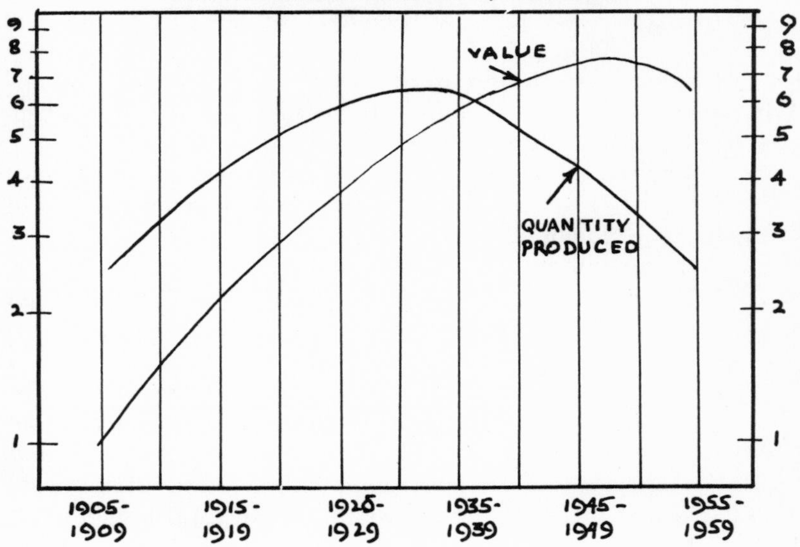

SOURCE: See Appendix A.

[a] Freehand curves based on five-year average.

the decreasing supply of all three species has resulted in a downward trend in the total value of the product.

Prices of canned salmon may well have reached levels in the 1950s at which consumer demand begins to exhibit some real measure of elasticity. At these high prices it is likely that a number of other protein foods are being substituted for salmon. Two prominent candidates are canned tuna, which is now obtained in much larger quantities and at far more favorable prices, and frozen fillets, which have become available in recent years in a wide range of quantities and prices and are beginning to be accepted as a standard food item by the consumer. A continuing weakness in poultry prices also may have led to some substitution. It is reasonable that this substitution effect would hit hardest at pink and chum, since the red salmon had already moved to a point where demand for it could be regarded as a specialty demand. The stronger price trend for reds undoubtedly reflects rising per capita incomes throughout the nation. On the other hand, chums and to a lesser extent pinks have traditionally been sold largely as a staple food in the lower income areas. With rising incomes there undoubtedly has been a tendency to shift away from cheaper fish to more desirable protein foods, as well as from the cheaper to the more expensive and higher quality grades of salmon.

These long-term trends in price and value indicate that the product has enjoyed a secular or relatively constant upward trend in demand which did not begin to slacken until the 1950s.

These trends also are of prime importance in understanding the increasing intensity of fishing effort, for the salmon fishery is carried on as a commerical venture, and fishing effort will contract or expand as profit opportunities widen or narrow. In this respect a common-property resource differs considerably from a resource that is privately owned. For example, a private owner of a valuable fishery resource would adjust his inputs in terms of gear units and labor in such a manner as to maximize his economic returns from the fishery, and in doing this he would use the smallest possible amount of the most efficient gear in an effort to maximize the difference between his total costs and total revenues. However, with a common-property resource in which there is no restriction on entry, the amount of fishing effort will be consistenly greater because the existence of profit in the fishery will attract additional units of gear until the profit is wiped out (i.e., at a point where total costs and total revenues are equal rather than where the difference is maximized as in the previous case). A maximum rather than a minimum amount of fishing effort is continually induced into the fishery and each individual fisherman receives only a bare minimum return sufficient to meet his costs and keep him in the fishery. Any increase in either prices or average catches or both which tends to increase the returns to the fishermen merely attracts more units of

FIGURE 16. SCHEMATIC DIAGRAM OF THE RELATIONSHIP BETWEEN TOTAL COSTS, TOTAL REVENUES, AND FISHING EFFORT

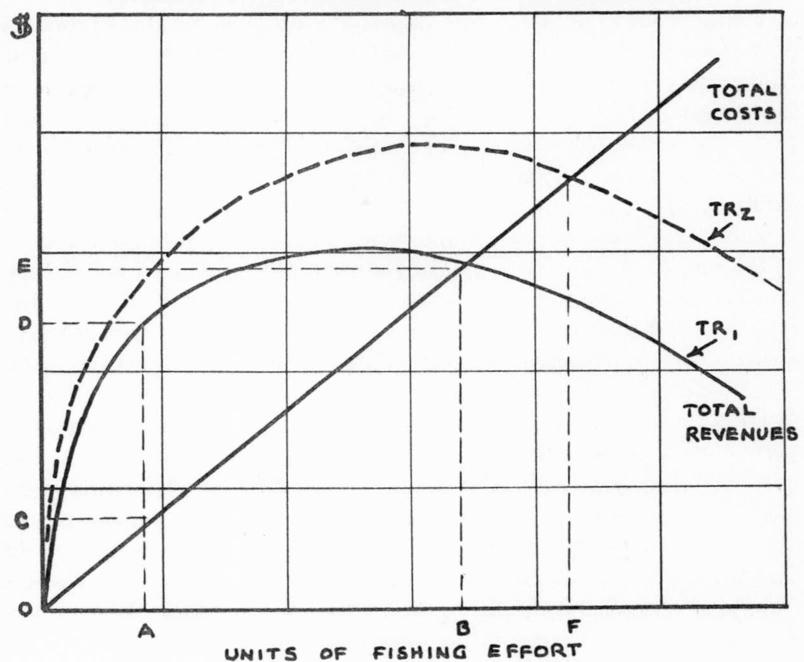

SOURCE: See Appendix A.

gear until total costs and total revenues are again equal. Similarly, any decrease in costs of fishing such as may occur through technological improvements in boats and gear will result in higher average catches and profits. This in turn will induce more gear into the fishery until the dollar returns to the fishermen are again at a minimum.[14]

These relationships are illustrated in the diagram in Figure 16. The price and cost conditions shown in the diagram are

[14] The reverse of these two examples is also true: an increase in costs or a decrease in price will result in a reduction of fishing effort under the conditions described because the fisherman would not be able to meet the costs of his operation.

assumed for the purposes of illustration and do not represent specific figures. A private owner of a resource would tend to operate at a fishing effort of OA units, because at this point the difference between total revenues (OD) and total costs (OC) is greatest. However, with free entry under a common property arrangement fishing intensity would increase from OA to OB where total costs and total revenues were equal,[15] and the profit that existed previously is simply dissipated in excessive costs through over-capitalization in fishing gear and men. If total revenues should increase to TR_2, the profits (or economic rent as it is more properly called) at fishing effort OB would tend to attract new gear into the fishery to a point OF where total costs and revenues were again equal. It is not difficult to visualize how other increases or decreases in either costs or revenues would influence fishing effort under the two property arrangements.

The Alaska salmon fishery has followed this theoretical model very closely. Until the mid-1930s the trends in both supply and demand were upward. The total value of production increased rapidly with most of the increase resulting from the growth in physical production. These economic conditions induced a rapid increase in the total amount of fishing effort. Two major market slumps occurred during this period—following World War I and during the early years of the depression in the 1930s—and both resulted in large decreases in production, prices, total value, and amount of fishing effort. But in each case the market conditions eventually improved and the upward trend in all these factors resumed.

In the late 1930s overexploitation of the resource resulted in a declining supply. Total production began to decrease rapidly, but the constant demand (which is influenced by conditions outside the fishery such as increasing population and per capita incomes, price of competing products, etc.) continued to rise. As a result of the interaction of these economic and biological conditions, the real price began to rise at an extremely rapid rate and this induced more fishermen and gear into the already overexploited fishery. These increasing fishing pressures tended to reduce the supply further, but prices were pushed higher and higher, and the total

---

[15] Assuming everything else remains constant.

FIGURE 17. COMPARISON OF REAL PRICES OF ALASKA SALMON WITH NUMBER OF FISHERMEN EMPLOYED, 1927–1958[a]

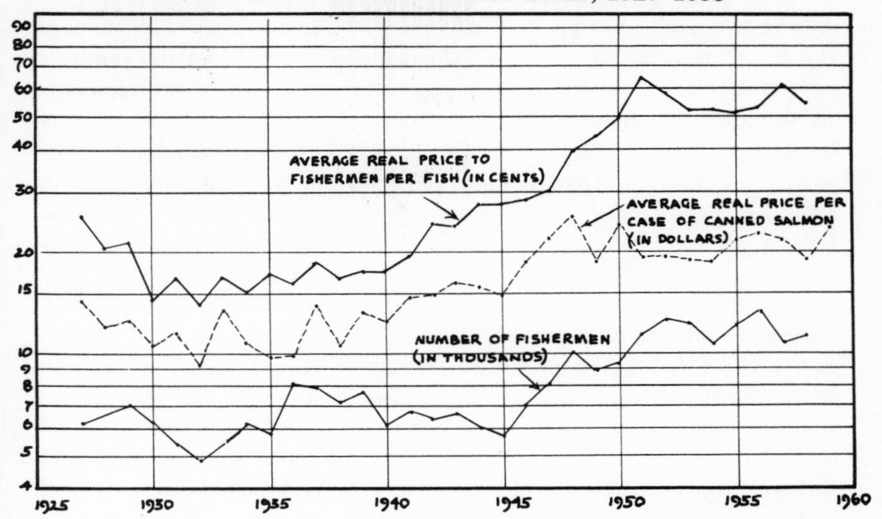

SOURCE: See Appendix A.

[a] All prices corrected to remove changes in the value of the dollar. (W.P.I., 1947–1949=100)

Price to fisherman based on value of catch, excluding value of trap-caught fish (which does not accrue to the fishermen).
Price per case based on weighted average of all five species of salmon.

value of production continued to increase in spite of the depleted state of the resource. As a result, the influx of fishermen and gear did not begin to moderate until the 1950s when prices showed signs of weakening. By this time the combined effect of a decreasing supply and slackening prices had culminated in a downward trend in the total value of production.

What happened during the period since the mid-1930s when the resource was being depleted at a rapid rate is illustrated in the four figures that follow. Figure 17 shows that the average real price paid to the fishermen increased steadily from around 18 cents per fish in the 1930s to a peak of around 70 cents per fish in the early 1950s. This amounts to an increase of nearly 300 per cent in the real price paid to the fishermen. During the same period the number of fishermen increased from approximately 7,500 to

12,000, or an increase of about 60 per cent. (The drop in the number of fishermen from 1940 to 1945 was the result of the manpower shortage during the war). Furthermore, the average real price to the fishermen has increased at a more rapid rate than the average real wholesale price of canned salmon. This reflects the shortage of salmon and the resulting vigorous competition for fish among owners of otherwise under-utilized canneries. Once a cannery operator is committed to the season's operation, he will bid very high for fish in order to make the largest pack possible even though this involves prices he would not have considered had he known they would prevail before he committed himself to the operation. The much firmer bargaining position of fishermen following the unionization movement in the 1930s also contributed to this stronger trend in prices to fishermen. In addition, traps were held at a constant level during this period, which further improved the fishermen's bargaining position.

Figure 18 shows the relation of the total wholesale value of canned salmon to the total value paid to the fishermen in real terms. The total value of the catch is also shown. (The difference between the value of the catch and the amount paid to fishermen represents the total value of trap-caught fish.) The total amount paid to fishermen has been increasing since 1935, whereas the total wholesale value of the canned product reached a peak in the 1940s and then began to decline. Thus, total returns to the processing sector have declined while the cost of raw fish has become a much greater part of the total costs of production. In the mid-1930s when salmon production was at its peak, the cost of fish to the canners amounted to less than 15 per cent of the total wholesale value of production, but by the late 1950s this cost had risen to over 30 per cent of the total value.

Figure 19 shows that even though the average catch per fisherman decreased from around 7,500 fish in the mid-1930s to about 2,500 fish in the 1950s, the fisherman's average real income from the salmon fishery has remained relatively stable owing to the rapid increase in fish prices. In the mid-1930s the fisherman received an annual average of $1,200 for his catch. This increased to around $1,800 in the mid-1940s and then decreased to around $1,400 in the 1950s. Thus, even though the number of fishermen increased by about 60 per cent and the average catch per fisherman decreased by about 70 per cent, the average real income from sal-

FIGURE 18. REAL WHOLESALE VALUE OF ALASKA CANNED SALMON COMPARED TO THE REAL VALUE OF THE CATCH AND THE REAL VALUE PAID TO THE FISHERMEN, 1927–1959[a]
(*in millions of dollars*)

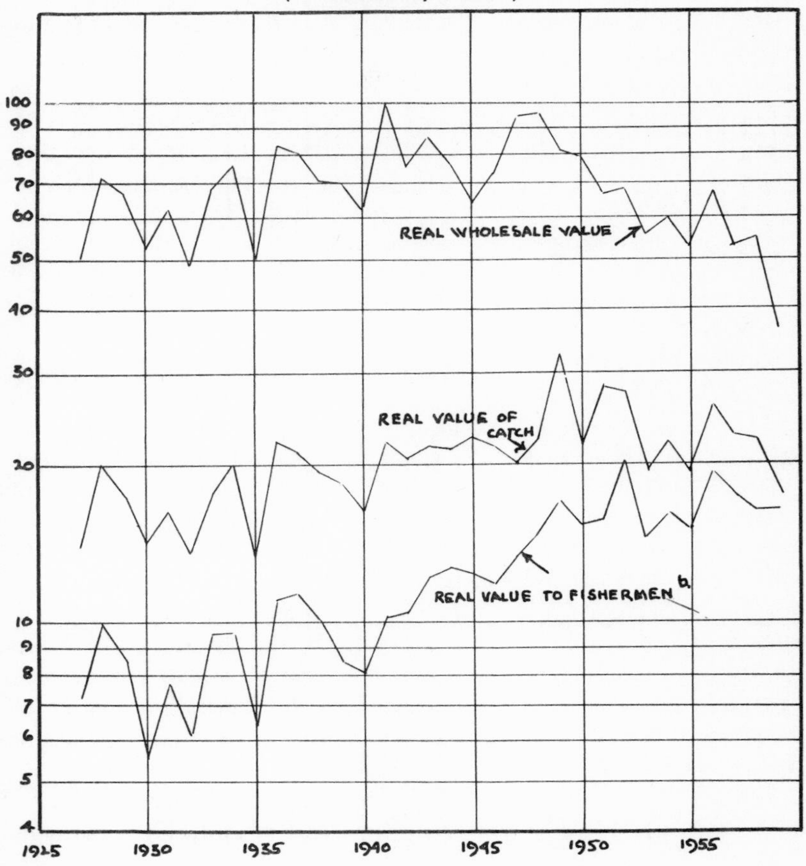

SOURCE: See Appendix A.

[a] All values corrected to remove changes in the value of the dollar. (W.P.I., 1947–1949=100)

[b] Excludes value of trap-caught fish (which does not accrue to the fishermen).

FIGURE 19. AVERAGE CATCH AND VALUE PER FISHERMAN COMPARED, 1927–1957

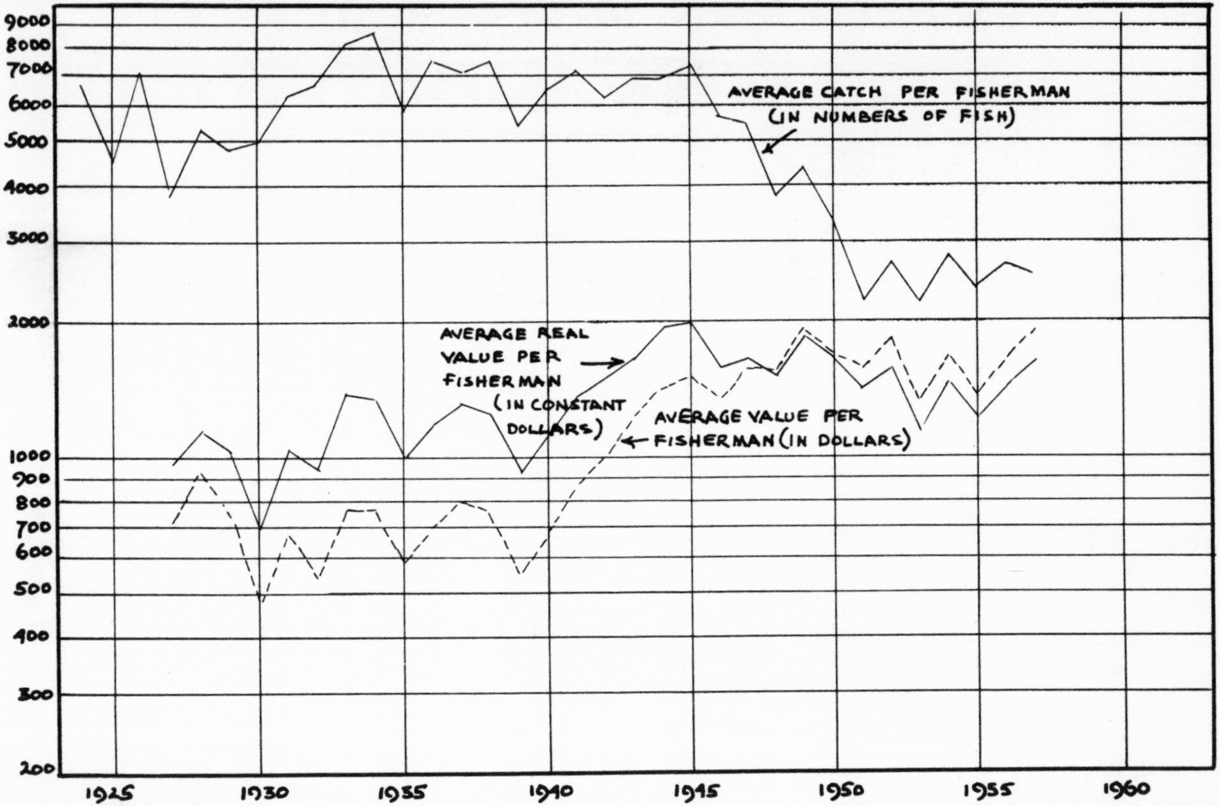

SOURCE: See Appendix A.

Average value—corrected with B.L.S. consumer price index (1947–1949=100)
Average catch—excludes trap-caught fish.

mon fishing has not declined. Fishing is a part-time occupation for many fishermen; therefore these average-income figures do not reflect total earnings. To reach any conclusions regarding the adequacy of the total income received by salmon fishermen it would be necessary to consider transfer payments such as employment compensation and social security as well as earnings from other occupations. The serious problem is the excessive numbers of men and gear in the fishery, and the resulting necessity to limit fishing time and efficiency of gear by government regulation, which has made the industry even more of a part-time occupation than seasonality requires.

Figure 20 shows the average pack and value of output per cannery in Alaska from 1927 to 1958. It illustrates the relative ease with which the processing sector of the industry has been able to adjust to changing profit prospects. This stands in sharp contrast to the behavior of the number of fishermen and units of gear in the fishery. The ability to reduce the number of plants after total output began to decline (with exception of the postwar boom period in the 1940s) reflects the ease with which consolidations could be handled, presumably without fear of antitrust action. In addition, the nature of the investment in a salmon cannery is such that the operation could be discontinued without excessive loss as declines in runs occurred. In the processing sector both capital and labor can be moved out of the industry entirely or from one area to another in response to profit opportunities much more readily than can fishermen and fishing gear. In this way the processing industry has been able to maintain a constant or slightly rising real value of output per cannery as the resource has declined.

It is apparent from this analysis that the level of fishing effort and hence the extent of overexploitation in the Alaska salmon fishery has depended as much on economic factors affecting costs and prices as on biological factors affecting physical yield. The salmon resource would not have been so heavily overfished if cost–price relationships had been less favorable. If the demand for salmon had leveled off in the 1920s, for example, it is possible that production would have stabilized at around three to four million cases, which may be somewhere near a level of maximum sustained yield. But with rising demand, exploitation was carried far beyond

FIGURE 20. AVERAGE PACK AND VALUE OF OUTPUT PER OPERATING CANNERY, 1927–1958[a]

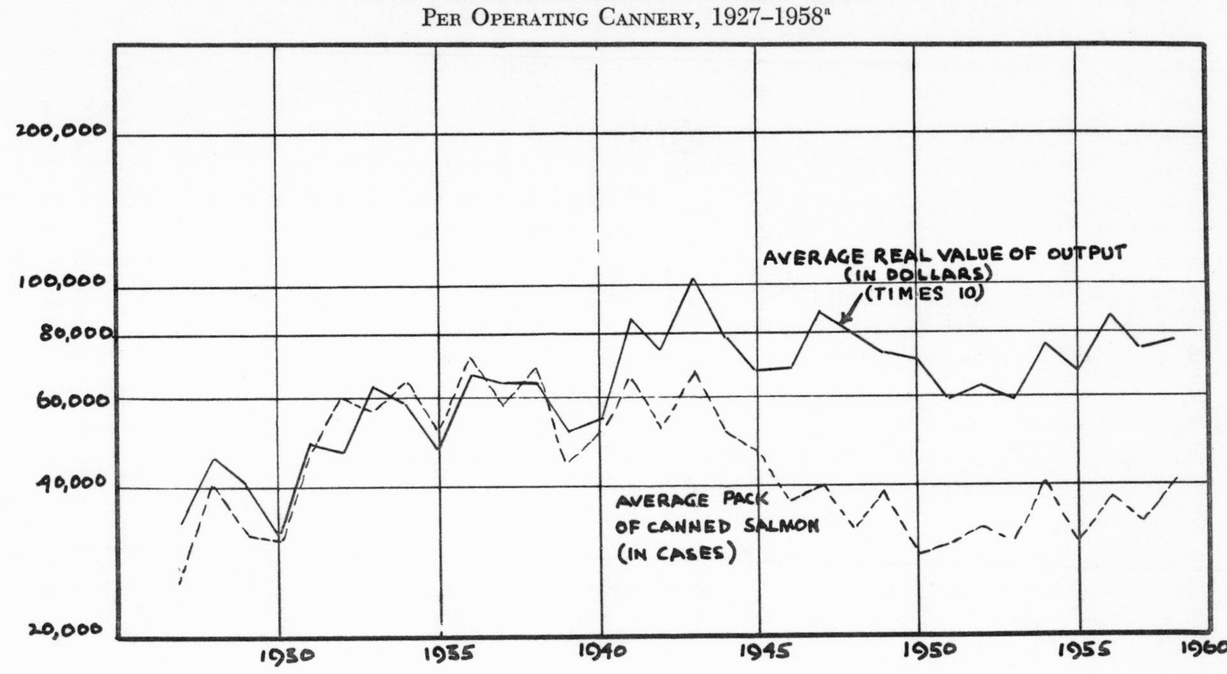

SOURCE: See Appendix A.

[a] Value corrected to show real value.

that point. As a result, more and more men and capital are engaged in taking fewer and fewer fish. Since demand for canned salmon will probably continue to increase, although somewhat more slowly than in the past, it may be expected that this situation will continue to worsen.

The core of the problem can be traced back to the peculiar common-property status of the resource. As long as fishing is regarded as accessible to anyone, the only way of preventing serious overfishing is to limit efficiency of men and gear in various ways. This may take the form of elimination of more efficient types of gear, limitations on the size of boats, limitations on the length and mesh size of gear, etc., all of which are designed to prevent use of the most efficient catching operations. More commonly in Alaska it has meant seasonal closures in which fishing is prohibited for as much as four or five days each week. But the regulatory authority cannot restrict entry.

The measures that have been adopted not only made the fishery more costly through overcapacity and under-utilization of boats, men, and gear, but the excess capacity put a tremendous pressure on enforcement since every vessel owner had a powerful incentive to violate. It has also led to heavy regional concentrations of gear as the fishermen hit the peaks of the successive runs in an effort to squeeze the largest possible output from their under-utilized equipment.

Dr. James Crutchfield of the University of Washington, one of the foremost fisheries economists in the United States, drew the following conclusion regarding the Alaska salmon fishery in a paper delivered at the Alaska Science Conference in 1959:

> Until and unless it becomes possible to reduce the amount of gear to the minimum needed to take the permitted catch, economic waste, widespread violation of regulations and a threat to the very existence of the industry will remain.
>
> This problem is not unique to the fisheries. In greater or lesser degree it has plagued the petroleum industry, the forest products industry and the use of public grazing land. In each of these cases, however, we have come, belatedly, to recognize that unrestricted access to a common-property resource is fatal to wise conservation of the resources and to efficiency in the use of other productive factors. Only in the fisheries do we find such heavy (and emotional) resistance to principles which

are fundamental to our free economy: that an industry should produce the right output at the lowest possible cost.[16]

With this background on the pattern of exploitation that emerged and some of the major biological, social, and economic factors influencing it, this study now turns to a political analysis of the efforts of the federal government to conserve the resource.

---

[16] James A. Crutchfield, "The Economics of Salmon Management" (unpublished paper delivered at the Alaska Science Conference, Juneau, Alaska, August 1959), p. 10.

PART TWO

LEGISLATION AND CONTROVERSY

4 *Early Conservation Efforts*

FOR NEARLY A QUARTER of a century after Alaska was purchased from Russia in 1867, Congress showed little interest in the new acquisition. There were few people living in Alaska other than the indigenous native population, and the territory was generally thought of as a worthless land of ice and snow. Except for the fur seals, which had been severely depleted before the purchase, little was known about the natural resources of the region. The salmon industry was allowed to develop with little public concern over the emerging pattern of exploitation.

In an act passed by Congress in 1868, Alaska was made a customs district under the Treasury Department. Among other duties the Secretary of the Treasury was given the function of supervising the fisheries but was provided with no specific regulatory authority.[1] The Treasury Department inherited the fisheries responsibilities mainly because it was the only federal agency operating in the territory at the time with the exception of the U.S. Navy. Although the department was in no way organized or staffed to carry out such a function, supervision of the fisheries remained lodged there until 1903 when Congress created the U.S. Bureau of Fisheries.

In the 1880s the United States Fish Commission began scientific

[1] 15 Stat. 240.

investigations in Alaska. During the ensuing years as commercial exploitation increased, the Secretary of the Treasury frequently suggested to Congress that the Fish Commission should take over the federal responsibilities of fishery management in Alaska; but the Fish Commission resisted the move. It conceived its role as one of pure scientific research and was reticent to enter into the actual policing and regulating of the fisheries. However, its investigations, reports, and recommendations were instrumental in calling attention to the need for conservation legislation.

The Fish Commission sent Dr. Tarleton Bean to the territory to investigate the condition of the salmon fisheries in the late 1880s. In his report Dr. Bean reviewed the progress of the industry northward. He called attention to the near destruction of the salmon runs from the Sacramento to the Columbia rivers and drew the following prophetic conclusion with respect to the future of the fishery in Alaska:

> Whether the fishery shall continue to furnish the opportunity for profitable enterprise and investment depends upon the policy to be inaugurated and maintained by the government. Under judicious regulation and restraint these fisheries may be made a continuing source of wealth to the inhabitants of the Territory and an important food resource to the nation: without such regulation and restraint we shall have repeated in Alaskan rivers the story of the Sacramento and the Columbia. . . . For a few years there will be wanton waste of the marvelous abundance which the fishermen—concerned only for immediate profit and utterly improvident of the future—declare to be inexhaustible. The season of prosperity will be followed by a rapid decline in the value and production of these fisheries, and a point will eventually be reached where the salmon canning industry will be no longer profitable.[2]

Of all the methods employed to make larger packs, the most destructive was the early practice of barricading streams, and it was this method of capturing salmon that was the subject of the first salmon-conservation legislation for Alaska. These log barricades were erected across a stream from bank to bank so that it was impossible for the salmon to ascend. As the salmon gathered in schools at the base of the barricades it was only necessary to dip them out into a scow and transport them to the nearby cannery.

---

[2] Tarleton H. Bean, *Report on the Salmon and Salmon Rivers of Alaska*, Bulletin of the U.S. Fish Commission, 1889 (Washington: U.S. Government Printing Office, 1889), p. 167.

These devices were used by the Indians prior to the commercial era. When used sparingly there was little danger to the salmon runs, but when used unregulated as a commercial device under highly competitive conditions they were lethal. By the late 1880s the misuse of barricades had reached serious proportions. It was clear that the situation could not be controlled without government regulation, and in 1889 Congress passed an Act making it unlawful to erect dams, barricades, or other obstructions in any of the rivers of Alaska for the purpose of preventing or impeding the ascent of salmon to their spawning grounds. The Secretary of the Treasury was authorized to estabish the necessary surveillance for enforcement of the law, and the Fish Commissioner was directed to investigate the Alaska salmon fisheries and recommend to Congress additional legislation necessary "to prevent the impairment or exhaustion of these valuable fisheries."[3]

Congress did not provide the Treasury Department with an appropriation to enforce the new law until 1892 when funds were made available for one inspector and an assistant. It was physically impossible for the two men to make anything but a token gesture toward enforcing the law along Alaska's lengthy coastline during the intense two- to three-month fishing season. The inspectors were not provided with government transportation and they were frequently obliged to depend upon the boats of the salmon packers to get from one cannery to another. Surprise visits were almost impossible. The ridiculousness of the situation was expressed by Special Agent Howard Kutchin in his report to the Secretary of the Treasury:

> A self-respecting man confronted by conditions that tend to make his pretensions ridiculous cannot but feel more-or-less like a humbug; and when he detects a sly smile of derision on the face of the person whom he is presumed to have somewhat under surveillance it is not calculated to puff him up with official self-importance. He can scarcely be regarded as an embodiment of the majority of the law when he must look to possible would-be law breakers for indispensable assistance in the performance of his duties.[4]

---

[3] 25 Stat. 1009 (March 2, 1889).

[4] Howard N. Kutchin, *Report on Salmon Fisheries of Alaska,* Treasury Department Document No. 2010 (Washington: U.S. Government Printing Office, 1898), p. 12.

In a report to Congress in 1892, the U.S. Fish Commissioner noted that existing agreements and consolidations among the cannery owners had placed a degree of limitation on the salmon catch but that this was actuated solely by selfish motives which could be abrogated at any time when prices recovered under the stimulus of increased demand. The Fish Commissioner recognized that the basic problem in conserving the salmon was to reduce and control fishing intensity, and he recommended that Congress consider giving authority to the Treasury Department to lease the privilege of taking salmon and to limit the catch for each lease.[5] However, these ideas were much too new and revolutionary, especially for an uninterested Congress, and no action was ever taken on them.

In 1894 Assistant Secretary of the Treasury Charles S. Hamlin visited Alaska for a personal inspection of the salmon fisheries, and shortly afterward the department issued a report concluding that the salmon fishery would soon end in disaster if left to the present system of law.[6] In the following year a bill was drawn up in the department based on the ideas and observations of the Assistant Secretary. It proposed considerable extension of the powers of the Secretary in regulating fishing effort and controlling fishing seasons. Before being transmitted to Congress, however, the bill was sent to the major canning corporations in San Francisco for their views. The response of the cannerymen varied. They seemed to be in favor of conservation in general, but when confronted with a specific proposal it was difficult to get agreement among them on specific measures. By the time the bill finally passed Congress in 1896 it contained only those provisions acceptable to a majority of the larger canners.[7]

The 1896 Act was directed at reducing commercial fishing efforts in the streams and rivers above tidewater where the danger of intensive fishing was greatest. The Act made it unlawful to fish for salmon in any creeks or streams of less than five hundred feet in width. Fishing was permitted in the larger rivers, but nets, traps, or other gear could not be stretched more than one-third of the

---

[5] Marshall McDonald, U.S. Commissioner of Fish and Fisheries, *Report on the Salmon Fisheries of Alaska, 1892* (Washington: U.S. Government Printing Office, 1892), p. 3 (Also in Senate Misc. Documents 52-1, v. 3, No. 192, p. 3).

[6] U. S. Congress, House, *Seal and Salmon Fisheries and General Resources of Alaska,* 35th Congress, 1st Sess., 1898, House Doc. 92, Part 2, p. 452.

[7] 29 Stat. 316, June 9, 1896.

width, and all fishing gear had to be at least one hundred yards apart at all times. A weekly closed period was provided, but the important fishing districts of Bristol Bay, Cook Inlet, and Prince William Sound were specifically excluded from this provision. On certain rivers and under specific circumstances the Secretary could limit the fishing season, establish closed periods, or prohibit fishing entirely, but again the more important fishing areas were excluded. While the Act provided the Secretary with a number of new powers, its limitations were serious. The greatest of these was that the Secretary could control fishing activities only in the rivers and streams. All fishing below the mean low tide line remained completely unregulated.

During the 1890s those concerned with the conservation of the Alaska salmon resource began to consider the possibilities of artificial propagation as a means of maintaining the yield of salmon. The biologists of the U.S. Fish Commission had made some encouraging advances with salmon hatchery experiments in California, and in 1892 the Fish Commissioner[8] proposed artificial propagation as a possible alternative solution to the conservation problem in Alaska. There was no scientific evidence that artificial propagation could be carried out successfully under conditions in Alaska, yet the Fish Commission continued to urge establishment of hatcheries in the territory. In their zeal to promote this new idea some of the scientists went so far as to intimate that an adequate hatchery program would reduce the need for government controls.[9] With this implication given to artificial propagation, the idea rapidly took hold and was soon being espoused by the cannery owners as the course of action the government should take instead of adopting more stringent regulations to protect the resource. From their point of view no more perfect solution to the conservation problem could be found than to have government limit itself to planting the seeds, permitting private industry to concern itself solely with harvesting of the annual crops.

The Treasury Department became convinced through the efforts

---

[8] McDonald, *op. cit.*, p. 16.

[9] For example see the statement of Dr. Barton Warren Evermann in: U.S. Congress, House, Committee on the Territories, *Amendment of Laws Relating to Fisheries and Other Occupations in Alaska, Hearings,* 61st Cong., 2nd Sess., 1910, pp. 23-25.

of the Fish Commission that hatcheries were a necessary adjunct to their regulatory program. In May 1900, the Secretary promulgated a regulation requiring each company taking salmon from Alaska waters to establish a suitable hatchery and to return red salmon to the spawning grounds at the rate of at least four times the number of fish taken the preceding season.[10]

It soon became apparent, however, that the hatchery regulation was almost impossible of enforcement. The regulation was mandatory, but few of the packers obeyed it: some because no suitable place was available in the area where the fish were being taken, others because establishment and operation of hatcheries would cost more than their returns from the fishery justified, and still others because of a lack of knowledge in hatchery work. The Treasury agent reported in 1903 that of forty companies engaged in packing salmon in Alaska only one had gone into the hatchery efforts with anything like earnest purpose and even this concern did not produce the ratio of red salmon fry required.[11]

The regulation was later rescinded, but the idea of hatcheries as a fundamental answer to the salmon conservation problem continued to grow. During the early 1900s over a dozen different bills were introduced in Congress with the purpose of inducing private citizens to invest capital and labor in artificial propagation work in Alaska. None of these became law, but the support each received from both government and industry was indicative of the hopeful enthusiasm the idea generated.

With the improvement of market conditions for canned salmon at the turn of the century, a rash of new canneries came into existence and packers were reported straining every nerve to exceed the previous year's pack. Cannery superintendents were ordered to can all the fish they could get or to face the prospect of losing their jobs.

Shortly after Theodore Roosevelt succeeded to the presidency he ordered the U.S. Fish Commission to make a thorough investigation of the Alaska salmon fishery and to recommend changes in the laws and regulations necessary to assure proper conservation.

---

[10] In 1902 the regulation was changed to require at least ten times the number of salmon taken the preceding season.

[11] Howard M. Kutchin, *Report on the Salmon Fisheries of Alaska, 1903,* Department of Commerce and Labor Document No. 12 (Washington: U.S. Government Printing Office, 1904), p. 21.

Dr. David Starr Jordan, eminent biologist at Stanford University, was appointed to conduct the study with the aid of the scientific staff of the Fish Commission. In his final report, submitted to the President in 1904, Dr. Jordan called attention to the appalling condition of the fishery and the inadequacy of the existing conservation measures.[12] It was recommended that the Secretary be given more authority to limit fishing and to close specific areas. The possibility of limiting the number of canneries in any particular area as a means of forcing conservation was mentioned as desirable, but the members of the study group hesitated to recommend this step wholeheartedly for fear that "it might place in the hands of the Secretary a very difficult and unwelcome task."[13] Greatest emphasis in the report was given to what was considered to be an urgent need to establish government hatcheries "in order to maintain the supply without the necessity of curtailing production."[14] It was felt that by artificial propagation such a large number of fry could be turned out that the fish destroyed by the canners would not be missed.

At the time this report was being prepared a government reorganization measure passed Congress which had a significant bearing on administration of the Alaska fisheries. In 1903 the U.S. Fish Commission was abolished and a new Department of Commerce and Labor was created with a Bureau of Fisheries as one of its integral divisions.[15] The new Bureau of Fisheries inherited the scientific responsibilities of the Fish Commission as well as many related fishery functions that had previously been scattered throughout the federal service. In addition, the responsibilities of regulating the Alaska fisheries was transferred from the Secretary of the Treasury to the Secretary of Commerce and Labor, and the new Bureau of Fisheries was designated to carry out these functions.

One of the advantages of this reorganization from the point of view of the Alaska salmon-conservation program was that for the first time it would be handled by fishery experts and scientists within an agency whose sole function was the fisheries. But the

[12] U.S. Congress, House, *Report of the Alaska Salmon Commission*, 54th Cong., 2nd Sess., Document No. 477, pp. 1-2.
[13] *Ibid.*, p. 29.
[14] Ibid., p. 17.
[15] 32 Stat. 552, Sec. 7, p. 828. (Act approved February 14, 1903.)

new arrangement was by no means perfect. The staff of the bureau was made up almost entirely of scientists from the old Fish Commission who were interested primarily in scientific research, and they brought with them an unwillingness to handle such mundane affairs as the policing and regulating of fishing in the territory of Alaska. This accounts in part for the great emphasis given to artificial propagation in the management of the Alaska salmon fishery during the next two decades.

However, the greatest disadvantage lay elsewhere. The primary function of the Department of Commerce and Labor was "to foster, promote and develop the foreign and domestic commerce, the mining, manufacturing, shipping and fishing industries . . . in the United States."[16] The department had few regulatory functions, and in time it became a general service agency ministering to the needs of its special clientele—the American businessman. The difficulties in formulating and carrying out a restrictive regulatory program within a promotional organization became exceedingly apparent in the years to follow.

Shortly after the reorganization, steps were taken to put into effect some of the major recommendations in Dr. Jordan's report to the President. Efforts were first directed toward the establishment of salmon hatcheries, and in 1905 the bureau succeeded in obtaining a special appropriation for the construction of two government-owned and -operated hatcheries in Alaska.[17]

In 1906 the bureau turned its attention to the passage of legislation to extend regulatory powers, and in that year a comprehensive Alaska fisheries conservation bill was introduced in the House of Representatives.[18] Unlike the program for government hatcheries, however, the proposed conservation legislation generated strong opposition among elements within the industry.

The bill provided for the extension of the Secretary's authority to cover fishing in all the waters of Alaska under United States jurisdiction (i.e., three miles out from the coastline). It provided that within these waters fishing activities would be subject to such rules and regulations as the Secretary might deem necessary to

---

[16] Merle Fainsod and Lincoln Gordon, *Government and the American Economy* (New York: W. W. Norton & Co., Inc., 1941), pp. 106-107.

[17] U.S. Department of Commerce and Labor, *Annual Report of the Secretary for 1905* (Washington: U.S. Government Printing Office, 1905), p. 37.

[18] H. R. 13543, 59th Cong., 1st Sess.

prevent exhaustion of the resource. The bill contained a number of specific prohibitions on certain types of fishing gear as well as extended weekly closed periods and other limitations. In addition, it provided that money collected from federal taxes on fisheries in Alaska should be placed in a special "Alaska Fisheries Fund" to be used under the direction of the Secretary for scientific studies, law enforcement, and artificial propagation work in Alaska.[19] Finally, in a provision designed to promote private hatchery work, it was proposed that cannery operators who established and maintained hatcheries would be eligible for tax rebates at the rate of forty cents per 1,000 red salmon fry liberated in the streams.

The legislative history of the bill illustrates the character and intensity of the conflict that was developing over the government's role in managing the Alaska salmon fishery. Hearings were held on the bill in Washington, D. C. in March of 1906 before the House Committee on the Territories. Scientists and other officials of the Bureau of Fisheries and the Department of Commerce and Labor presented strong statements in support of the bill, and they pressed for immediate action on the part of Congress to provide the bureau with the authority needed to prevent the industry from destroying the resource. The solicitor for the department pointed out that under existing law the regulatory authority of the Secretary was limited to fishing operations wholly within the rivers and streams, yet nearly all the fishing was being conducted outside this jurisdiction in the narrow channels and bays and around the mouths of the rivers and streams. He concluded:

> As the matter now stands the Department is expressly directed by the Act creating it to foster, promote and develop the fishing industry, without having the authority to enact regulations to prevent or prohibit practices which are detrimental to the industry.[20]

---

[19] In 1899 Congress enacted a general tax law affecting some forty businesses in Alaska to help defray the costs of territorial government. (Alaska Criminal Code, Act of March 3, 1899, Sec. 460). Under this law the salmon canners were taxed at four cents per case of salmon packed. This was the only tax canners were subjected to in Alaska. The money collected from these business taxes went into a special "Alaska Fund" to be used for schools, hospitals, roads, etc. The bill in question proposed that fishery tax monies would be diverted from the "Alaska Fund" to the special "Alaska Fisheries Fund" to constitute a permanent appropriation for fisheries conservation work only.

[20] U.S. Congress, House, Committee on the Territories, *Fisheries in Alaska, Hearings,* 59th Cong., 1st Sess., 1906, Part I, p. 10.

This request for additional authority was emphatically opposed by representatives of the Alaska salmon canners. C. W. Dorr, the vice president and general counsel of the Alaska Packers Association, objected to the proposed extension of the Secretary's authority to cover all waters of Alaska on the grounds that it represented an unwarranted and unconstitutional delegation of the law-making power to an executive agency. He complained that such a carte-blanche provision would make it possible for the bureau to promulgate regulations that would put people out of business, destroy their occupation, and cause serious financial loss, and that Congress would be unable to do anything about it.[21] He was opposed to the provision prohibiting fishing off the mouths of the rivers and streams, maintaining that existing laws and regulations were adequate for the purposes of conservation. He told the committee there had been no diminution of the salmon supply in Alaska. In fact, according to Dorr, salmon were going up the rivers in such enormous schools they were actually destroying each other on the spawning grounds, and any further restriction would only increase this wasteful destruction.[22] When questioned further by a member of the committee about the effects of fishing on salmon stocks, Dorr replied that "no more salmon are caught in all Alaska than the number of mosquitoes you could catch in your two hands by jumping into a big cloud of the insects and grabbing."[23]

To the salmon packers, less restriction on fishing and more emphasis on artificial propagation was the answer to the problem. M. G. Munly, who represented a half dozen different packing firms, told the committee it should "eliminate all of the radical restrictive features of the bill and provide for artificial propagation."[24] To substantiate this approach both Dorr and Munly quoted extensively from previous statements of government scientists, concerning the efficacy of salmon hatcheries in Alaska. The only feature of the bill receiving the full support of salmon packers was the provision allowing a tax rebate to those who established and operated hatcheries.

Dr. Evermann, chief scientist for the bureau, took exception to

[21] *Ibid.*, Part II, pp. 25-26.
[22] *Ibid.*, Part II, pp. 13-17.
[23] *Ibid.*, Part II, p. 40.
[24] *Ibid.*, Part II, p. 56.

the complacent attitude of the packers, noting that many salmon streams had already been abandoned by the canners because they failed to supply enough fish to make it an economic operation. He told the congressmen that figures showing annual increases in the salmon packs, used by the packers to support their negative position, were not a valid indicator of the condition of the resource and served only to mask depletion occurring in specific areas.[25]

Members of the House committee apparently were impressed with the objections raised by the salmon packers. At the conclusion of the hearings the chairman instructed the bureau officials to confer with the representatives of the canning industry "with a view to perfecting the bill."[26]

Coming .to a compromise was not easy. The bureau held out for two provisions which, it felt, were absolutely necessary. One was the section giving the Secretary authority to control fishing effort in all the waters of Alaska, and the other was the section providing for an Alaska Fishery Fund. The bureau felt that the former would provide the necessary flexibility to promulgate fishery regulations, while the latter would assure that financial means would be available to carry out the program. To maintain these two provisions intact the bureau yielded to the demands of the industry on almost all other counts, and the weakened version was reintroduced in the House.

The Committee on the Territories recommended passage of the substitute measure, stating in its report to the House that "all interests are now fully agreed upon the fairness and efficiency of the proposed bill as an adequate measure for the regulation of the great fisheries of Alaska."[27] While the bureau may not have agreed with this statement, nevertheless it was satisfied that the substitute bill at least contained the minimum provisions necessary to embark upon a more meaningful conservation program. But the bureau was slated for a big surprise.

Objection was made on the floor of the House that too much arbitrary power was being vested in the hands of the Secretary by extending his authority to the three-mile limit, and before the bill passed the House it was amended to reduce his regulatory

[25] *Ibid.*, Part II, pp. 41-51.
[26] *Ibid.*, Part II, p. 41.
[27] U.S. Congress, House, *House Report No. 2657*, 59th Cong., 1st Sess., p. 1.

authority to an area within five hundred yards off the mouths of all rivers and streams.[28] In the Senate it was again amended to strike out the provision establishing a special Alaska Fishery Fund,[29] and the bill, as amended by the House and Senate, became law on June 26, 1906.[30]

The Act bore little resemblance to the original comprehensive proposal drawn up by the bureau. It was primarily a codification of previous laws and regulations. It incorporated the four-cent tax on each case of canned salmon which had been enacted in 1899,[31] but an important clause was added providing that the tax would be "in lieu of all other licenses, fees and taxes," and canners who established and operated hatcheries became eligible for tax rebates. The only significant extention of authority was the provision allowing the Secretary to regulate fishing within five hundred yards of the mouths of the rivers and streams, a very limited extension in light of the increasing amounts of fishing gear attracted to the fishery each year. Obviously enough fishing gear operating unrestricted just outside the five-hundred-yard limit could deplete the salmon runs no matter what restrictive measures the Secretary might promulgate within his limited jurisdiction. It was not many years after passage of the Act that this precise condition prevailed and the bureau had no legal means to deal with the situation. The 1906 Act provided ample testimony to the growing political strength of the canned-salmon industry.

---

[28] U.S. *Congressional Record,* 59th Cong., 1st Sess., pp. 6486-6487.
[29] *Ibid.,* p. 8340.
[30] 34 Stat. 263.
[31] See fn. 19, p. 79.

5 *Conflict and Compromise*

DURING THE EARLY YEARS of commercial exploitation the rate of growth in the industry had been limited by the lack of well-developed markets. Prices of canned salmon fluctuated widely and overproduction was one of the greatest problems of the growing number of packers. This led to periodic consolidation moves and other voluntary efforts by the canners to hold down production. Shortly after the turn of the century, however, market conditions were greatly improved and the industry entered a period of dynamic growth. Great technological strides were made in both the catching and the processing of salmon, the price of the product was rising, and each year the outlook for profits was better than the last.

A number of factors account for these favorable market conditions. First, the industry, with the aid and cooperation of the federal government, undertook a worldwide advertising and promotional campaign which was highly successful in expanding both domestic and foreign markets. Second, even though the price of canned salmon was rising steadily during the period, the price to the consumer remained below that of meat and other competing products. Third, the exposure of unsanitary conditions in the meat-packing industry served to shift demand to other protein products such as fish. The salmon market was benefited accordingly. Finally, because of the ease of shipment and storage of canned salmon, an almost unlimited market developed for the product during World War I, and prices soared to unexpected heights.

The *Pacific Fisherman*, official trade journal of the canned-salmon industry since the turn of the century, reported in 1909 that the salmon packers had fought a winning battle for the conquest of the world's markets and that canned salmon was now a well-established staple article of food. It was concluded that the industry had developed to a point where "it is not a question of how to sell more salmon, but how to pack more."[1] In 1911 it was reported that the pack was the most profitable the canners had ever put up in Alaska and that "the canners are already preparing to increase their present plants or to build additional ones in time for next season, while a number of new concerns are preparing to invade the Territory."[2] Some weakness in the market began to show around 1914, which caused a ripple of concern within the industry, but this was erased the following year by the tremendous demand brought about by the war. The rapid increase in the number of canneries, the amount of fishing gear, and the size of the annual packs which occurred during this period are discussed in Chapter 3.

Such favorable business conditions were not conducive to any deep concern over the question of conservation among those exploiting the resource. Each year brought new demands which resulted in increased preparations for the next year; there seemed to be no end to the cycle of plenty. The salmon packers were unwilling to forgo profits as long as there were fish to catch, and they were in no mood to have any added interference from the federal government that might lead to a curtailment of their highly profitable operations.

This helps to account for the packers' opposition to the 1906 Act as originally introduced. It also helps to explain why the bureau was unable to get any additional regulatory authority for the next eighteen years even though bills to accomplish this were introduced in almost every session of Congress.

The conservation program conducted by the Bureau of Fisheries provided little restriction or guidance, and even the meager pro-

[1] *Pacific Fisherman*, November 1909, p. 13.
[2] *Ibid.*, October 1911, p. 16.

visions of the 1906 Act were poorly enforced. Until 1910 an annual appropriation of only $7,000 was provided to maintain one agent and an assistant to enforce the laws. The two men were stationed in Washington, D.C., and each year they made the long trek to Alaska to provide what surveillance they could over fishing and packing operations. In 1913 the appropriation for this work was increased to around $25,000, and the number of men increased to four, but this was still negligible in light of the increasing pressure that was being put upon the resource. Secretary of Commerce William C. Redfield admitted in his 1914 annual report that supervision exercised by the bureau over the Alaska salmon fisheries had been more alleged than real.[3] He made personal pleas to senators and congressmen from the Pacific coast states in an effort to gain their backing for an increased appropriation, but to no avail. The Commissioner of Fisheries summed up the problem in 1915 when he said:

> The farmers see to it that the Department of Agriculture is provided with means and men necessary for the discharge of its functions. The fishermen leave the Bureau of Fisheries to secure its appropriations through its unaided efforts.[4]

Occasional attempts to enforce the laws revealed how grossly they were being violated. A case in point occurred in the 1908 season when the agent decided to make a surprise investigation of the fishing activities in the waters of southeast Alaska. Visits to thirty-four traps revealed that twenty-nine were brazenly violating the law, four were guilty of minor violations and only one was conforming to the letter of the law. On a second surprise check of the same area only a few weeks later, twenty-four of the traps were found still openly violating the law. The agent stated in his report that the most reprehensible feature of all these violations was that on the second visit every one of the canneries was glutted with fish, and although they were unable to brail the traps more often than two or three times a week, the traps were operating

---

[3] U.S. Department of Commerce, *Annual Report of the Secretary, 1941* (Washington: U.S. Government Printing Office, 1915), p. 13. (Under a reorganization in 1913 all labor activities were transferred out of the Department of Commerce and Labor and the Bureau of Fisheries was retained in the new Department of Commerce. 37 Stat. 736.)

[4] *Pacific Fisherman*, February 1915, p. 22.

during the closed period as well as the open season.[5] Other examples of wholesale violations were reported periodically in the annual reports.

The circumstance with regard to bureau expenditures for research and scientific investigation of the salmon fishery was even more appalling. Between 1906 and 1915 a total of only $4,564.30 was spent for this purpose in Alaska.[6] This amounted to less than $500 a year. Indeed, it was not until 1921 that the bureau undertook its first serious, well-planned scientific study to determine the proportion of the salmon run escaping to the spawning beds on a particular river, and the relation between the size of the escapement and the returning run on the next cycle.[7]

This situation led Alaska's congressional delegate to charge on the floor of the House that while bureau officials constantly mentioned in their reports and elsewhere the vast amount of scientific knowledge the bureau possessed on the Alaska fisheries, when they were called on the carpet at congressional hearings they frequently were unable to provide adequate answers about the life and habits of the salmon. He concluded: "The average Alaska coast Indian knows all the Bureau of Fisheries scientists know about salmon, except their Latin names, and probably much more."[8]

Hatcheries and artificial propagation of salmon were given the greatest emphasis in the bureau's Alaska program, and in this effort it was able to gain the support of all segments in the industry. Between 1906 and 1920 total expenditures for maintenance and operation of government hatcheries in Alaska amounted to approximately $525,000 (excluding construction costs), and another $600,000 in tax rebates was paid to the larger canning concerns for operating similar private hatcheries.[9] When these figures are compared with the meager sums available during the same period for both law enforcement and scientific study, it becomes clear what great reliance was placed on artificial propagation. Unfor-

---

[5] Millard C. Marsh and John H. Cobb, *Fisheries of Alaska in 1908,* U.S. Bureau of Fisheries Document 645 (Washington: U.S. Government Printing Office, 1909), p. 34.

[6] See the schedule in the statistical Appendix.

[7] The study was undertaken by Dr. C. H. Gilbert on the Karluk River.

[8] U.S. *Congressional Record,* 63rd Cong., 3rd Sess., p. 705.

[9] Compiled from annual issues of *Alaska Fisheries and Fur Seal Industries, op. cit.*

tunately, not until around 1920 did the bureau begin to realize that this seemingly simple panacea was not working. At a meeting of the American Association for the Advancement of Science in that year, Dr. Barton W. Evermann, director of the California Academy of Science and a former head of the Alaska Division of the Bureau of Fisheries, questioned the efficacy of salmon hatcheries in the territory. He concluded that a close study of the situation showed that "after a number of years' operation the runs of Red Salmon upon which the hatcheries operated were smaller than when they began."[10] Subsequent studies led to the same conclusion, and in 1924 the Commissioner of Fisheries concluded bluntly that conservation of Alaska salmon "is not an artificial propagation problem; it is a problem wherein a sufficient escapement should be provided to take care of the spawning beds because it would be too expensive to provide otherwise."[11] Meanwhile, the Bureau of Fisheries had squandered much of its limited funds and personnel on a scientifically unproved principle.

Worst of all, however, this misplaced reliance on hatcheries tended to generate an attitude that the industry could have its cake and eat it too. For example, a lead article in the *Pacific Fisherman* in 1911 was entitled: "Hatcheries Make Extermination of Salmon Impossible."[12] A government official was quoted as saying that successes with artificial propagation proved there was absolutely no reason for depletion of the resource from overfishing, and that actually the supply of fish could be increased. He concluded that "there need be no fear felt as to the future if the various state governments and the federal government will maintain the proper hatchery system."[13] A year later when the *Chicago Tribune* came out with a strongly worded editorial claiming that nothing was being done to conserve the Alaska salmon and that the inevitable time was coming "when the story of the buffalo will be true of the salmon," a rejoinder was immediately printed in the industry trade journal:

---

[10] Reported in *Pacific Fisherman*, July 1920, p. 34.

[11] U.S. Congress, House, Committee on The Merchant Marines and Fisheries, *Fisheries of Alaska, Hearings . . . on H.R. 2741*, 68th Cong., 1st Sess., 1924, p. 8.

[12] *Pacific Fisherman*, November 1911, p. 10.

[13] *Ibid.*, p. 10.

Much is being done to conserve the fish. The United States has hatcheries and many fishing concerns maintain their own hatcheries. For every grown fish taken from Alaska waters, a hundred eggs are left in the spawning grounds.[14]

The bureau was having difficulty distinguishing between its general promotion function and its more specific responsibility to regulate the Alaska salmon fishery. As a promotion agency the bureau had undertaken to gain the support of the fishery interests behind its various service programs, and this drew the officials of the agency into close personal contact with the Alaska salmon packers. This is normal procedure for a service agency, but in the special case of the Alaska salmon fishery the atmosphere was not conducive to the formulation and execution of a vigorous, objective regulatory program. Instead it led to a search for some way to conserve without restricting, and the hatchery program suited this need admirably.

Statements of Dr. Hugh M. Smith, Commissioner of Fisheries, amply demonstrate the point. Dr. Smith, a scientist with a record of continuous service with the old Fish Commission and the bureau since 1886, had risen to the commissionership in 1913. In a speech in Seattle at a banquet given in his honor by the salmon canners shortly after he became commissioner, he said artificial propagation was the most effective way the federal government could aid the fishing industry and that this aspect of the bureau's operation in Alaska would be expanded.[15] Again the next year at a similar banquet in Seattle, Dr. Smith told the cannerymen:

I cherish the firm conviction that these fisheries which give Alaska its world-wide eminence, and which must necessarily influence the future in even a larger measure than they have influenced the past prosperity of Alaska, can be maintained without resorting to any herculean performances. In fact, the task, as I see it, is simple. . . . *The perpetuation of the Alaska salmon fisheries can be achieved . . . without any general or material curtailment of fishing operations or reduction of output.*[16]

This was exactly what the packers wanted to hear, and the trade journal was quick to praise Dr. Smith as a practical scientist to whom the industry was "under deep obligation . . . for the wise and intelligent interest he has displayed in their welfare."[17] Dr. Smith's

[14] *Ibid.*, November 1912, p. 32.
[15] *Ibid.*, July 1914, p. 13.
[16] *Ibid.*, May 1915, p. 12 (italics added).
[17] *Ibid.*, June 1914, p. 14.

actions and statements dispelled earlier fears in the industry that he would make the bureau too scientific.

The strong emphasis given to the promotional role was apparent in other aspects of the bureau's activities. In 1914 the industry prevailed upon the bureau to undertake a worldwide advertising campaign to popularize canned salmon, and the agency prepared and published over 100,000 copies of a canned-salmon bulletin which were distributed at the bureau's expense to all major newspapers in the United States and selected foreign countries.[18] The Commissioner of Fisheries sent a letter to the industry trade journal informing the packers that the canned-salmon bulletin was being sent to every part of the world and that the agency was doing its utmost to assist in enlarging the markets and obtaining more favorable terms for the product.[19] The editor responded that the government advertising program provided the greatest boost canned salmon ever had.

The packers and officials of the regulating agency were drawn into even closer relationship through the movement of the office of the Alaska division of the bureau from Washington, D. C., to Seattle. In 1914 the packers sent a representative to Washington to press for the move. The trade journal noted at the time that

> the calls for information and aid from Alaska operators are many, and, unfortunately, the Bureau has, through lack of officials of proper rank in this city, failed largely to meet these demands, and as a result considerable dissatisfaction is expressed by the more outspoken operators over the long delay when matters are submitted to Washington.[20]

Shortly thereafter, the Secretary of Commerce ordered a Pacific coast branch of the Bureau of Fisheries to be established at Seattle to handle the Alaska operations. When the new bureau office was opened in Seattle it was housed in the same building where twenty of the major salmon-packing concerns had their principal offices, as well as those of the American Can Company, the *Pacific Fisherman,* and various associations of salmon canners.[21]

The extent to which the packers had succeeded in gaining the confidence of bureau officials was revealed vividly at congressional

---

[18] *Ibid.,* February 1914, p. 21.
[19] *Ibid.,* April 1914, p. 11.
[20] *Ibid.,* January 1914, p. 24.
[21] *Ibid.,* February 1917, p. 34.

hearings in 1916. The Committee on Merchant Marine and Fisheries was considering a controversial bill dealing with traps in Alaskan waters. A large contingent of packers and their representatives were on hand to testify. Referring to these men, the Deputy Commissioner of Fisheries, E. Lester Jones, said in his testimony before the Committee:

> I have had the pleasure of meeting a great many of the men who are interested in the fishery interests of the West Coast, and I have generally found them a substantial type of businessman . . . who is not going to deliberately injure his investment. . . . These gentlemen here today (cannery lobbyists) are conversant with the business, the habits of the salmon, etc., and I might truthfully say that there are no better authorities in the country on these matters. They are really helpful to the government . . . in working out these problems, and their counsel should be encouraged, not discouraged. *I do not believe that their motives are anything but broad ones, looking to the future preservation of the salmon.*[22]

The salmon canners had wasted no time in developing an effective organization to protect and promote their interests, and this helps to account for the success the industry was having in its relations with the bureau. The first recognition for the need to organize came in 1910 when a bill was introduced in Congress to increase the meager tax on canned salmon in Alaska. The additional funds to be derived from the tax would be used in supporting schools, roads, welfare, and other expanding public needs in the territory. The industry trade journal called the proposed tax measure a major emergency requiring immediate and concerted action on the part of the Alaska cannerymen to defeat the measure. The editorial concluded that for a number of years the industry had needed a formal organization to look after its interests in legislative and other government matters, and that such a move could no longer be neglected.[23]

In the summer of 1911 the National Canners Association sent an official to Seattle to help organize the salmon canners of the Pacific Northwest into a single association to cooperate with the national organization on the legislative level "to prevent the pas-

---

[22] U.S. Congress, House, Committee on the Merchant Marine and Fisheries, *Alaska Fisheries, Hearings on H.R. 9528,* 64th Cong., 1st Sess., 1916, p. 348. (italics added).

[23] *Pacific Fisherman,* April 1910, p. 13.

sage of really harmful if well meant regulations."[24] Even the government urged the canners to organize. At a speech before the cannerymen in 1912 the chief of the Alaska Division of the Bureau of Fisheries called for greater support from the canners for the bureau's work in Alaska, emphasizing the necessity of unity of purpose among the canners in securing assistance from the government in developing the industry.[25] Shortly thereafter the Association of Alaska Salmon Canners was formed to work cooperatively with the Puget Sound Salmon Canners Association. A permanent legal staff was retained to represent the cannerymen in Washington, D.C., and the packers pledged to share the expenses.

In 1913 another organization known as the Oregon–Washington–California Coast Salmon Canners Association was set up. The industry trade journal concluded that the salmon-canning industry of the Pacific coast was now able to present a united front for the first time in the history of the business: "It is in the cooperation of these powerful organizations . . . that the greatest good of the industry rests. . . . Harmony will now prevail where the biggest broadest questions prevail."[26]

In 1914 the Association of Pacific Fisheries was organized to embrace all the important fishery interests along the coast, including salmon, halibut, and cod among others. Headquarters for the new association was located in Seattle. Its principal objective was to improve and perpetuate the fishing industry along the Pacific coast, and to promote the welfare of the individual members by all legal means.[27]

Through this hierarchy of associations the Alaska salmon canners were able to exert tremendous influence in the political process, and they did not hesitate to use this newly acquired power to the fullest. On controversial issues before Congress or the administration dealing with the Alaska fisheries, the salmon canners frequently were able to gain the support of a majority of West coast senators and congressmen, and invariably at least one of these held a key position on one of the congressional committees handling fishery legislation. Senator Wesley L. Jones from Washington, for

---

[24] *Ibid.*, July 1911, p. 16.
[25] *Ibid.*, December 1912, p. 22.
[26] *Ibid.*, February 1913, p. 22.
[27] *Ibid.*, August 1914, p. 17.

example, was chairman of the Senate Committee on Fisheries throughout this period. Most of the Alaska salmon canners were his constituents.

Controversy over the program to conserve the salmon resource originated not through any basic disagreement between the bureau and the canned-salmon industry, but through a strong dissatisfaction within the territory itself. To understand the conflict that developed it is necessary to review briefly the origin of the territorial viewpoint.

In 1884 Congress passed the first Organic Act for Alaska which provided a very limited form of government under a federally appointed governor.[28] As the population of the territory began to grow, a strong demand arose for some form of local self-government. In 1906 Congress authorized a voteless congressional delegate to be elected by the people of Alaska to represent their interests in the House of Representatives.[29] The delegate immediately began to press for congressional action to provide an adequate form of territorial government, and for increased local taxes to provide for public programs and services that were needed in Alaska. At about the same time a reaction developed within the territory against the way the salmon resource was being exploited. There was concern over the lack of adequate conservation measures to protect the resource, and there was concern because very little of the proceeds from this resource were accruing to the residents of the territory.

In 1911 the Governor of Alaska, Walter E. Clark, appealed to President Taft to influence Congress to pass a law protecting the salmon fisheries, which, he said, were being seriously injured from lack of proper safeguards. He told the President that the output of salmon should not be allowed to increase beyond the present size, yet he noted that each year many new canneries were being established. He urged the framing of a new law requiring persons and corporations desiring to establish canneries in Alaska to obtain a license from the Secretary of Commerce. In this manner, he said, the Secretary could keep close watch on the development of the industry and exclude canners from districts in which the supply of fish was already meeting a heavy annual drain.[30] In 1913

[28] 31 Stat. 321.

[29] 34 Stat. 169.

[30] *Pacific Fisherman,* October 1911, p. 13.

the fishermen expressed their deep concern over the economic situation in a letter addressed to the Governor:

Salmon were formerly the principal food of the natives, but since the advent of the canneries the natives are no longer so plentifully supplied; nearly everything inside the canneries is performed by Chinese and Japanese contract labor brought from San Francisco. . . . hardly any of this work being offered to the residents of Alaska; every year the locating of more fish traps by the canneries is making this important industry in Alaska a monopoly of nonresident and foreign corporations whose great wealth has been taken from the waters of Alaska by the operation of canneries a few months annually. If the natives are deprived of an opportunity to fish for a living, the Government will have to support them; if the white residents are deprived of that opportunity, they will have to leave the homes they have worked hard to get.[31]

In 1914 the Governor pointed out in his annual report to the Secretary of the Interior that conservation had been applied to nearly every natural resource in Alaska save the fisheries—the one resource, he said, which called most loudly for the protecting care of the government. He concluded:

The waters of Alaska have been exploited for their wealth for many years and they have yielded many millions of dollars, and large individual fortunes have been accumulated therefrom. At no time, however, have the exploiters contributed anything like an adequate return for the privileges they have enjoyed. . . .

In the desire for gain on the part of most of the exploiters of the fisheries of Alaska, the conservation of these fishes seems to have been practically lost sight of.[32]

The character and intensity of the developing conflict was aptly illustrated in 1916 when the Governor of Alaska, John F. Strong, made a direct frontal attack on the Bureau of Fisheries and its policies. In preparing his annual report for that year the Governor had called for a statement from the bureau concerning the status of the salmon fishery in Alaska. The bureau reported to the Governor with the following review of the condition of the resource:

It is not uncommon to hear it stated by some persons that the fishing resources of Alaska are suffering so severely, as a result of ruthless commercial exploitation, that the day is close at hand when this valuable

[31] U.S. Department of the Interior, *Annual Report of the Governor of Alaska, 1913* (Washington: U.S. Government Printing Office, 1913), p. 529.

[32] *Ibid.*, 1914, pp. 339, 355.

natural resource will almost cease to exist. Such opinion very often emanates from the tourist who passes through Alaska and may stop for a few hours at two or three salmon canneries. . . . He fails to appreciate the tremendous number of salmon which the waters are capable of yielding without suffering depletion. The real fact of the situation, as developed by those in authority who are competent to pass upon the matter is that, while occasionally there may be a stream or a section that is not so richly productive of salmon or other fish as formerly, yet, in the main, the waters of Alaska are not yet made to yield their maximum of fishery products without being depleted.[33]

Governor Strong took special exception to the bureau's optimism, and in his annual report he quoted the bureau's statement and concluded with the following analysis of his own:

A matter of vital economic and industrial importance to Alaska is the conservation of its . . . salmon fisheries. In discussing it, I am well aware that my opinion as to the depletion of salmon is in direct variance with that of the United States Bureau of Fisheries. . . .

The statement of fishermen . . . whose actual observation of fishery conditions in Alaska extends over a period of many years, challenges the bureau's point of view, and this is also strengthened by the results of observation and experience of at least one of the fishery inspectors who has been stationed in Alaska for a number of years. . . . The opposite view to that of the Bureau of Fisheries may be summed up as follows.

Salmon fisheries in Alaska . . . are being rapidly depleted and probably a great deal more rapidly than the Bureau of Fisheries realizes. The few statistics available to the Bureau cannot show this growing scarcity of the salmon, and, in fact, may even be misleading to the extent of giving the impression of an increase. It is true that the statistics of the packs for a number of years past show, as a rule, an increase in the annual production of canned salmon, but, as against this condition, it must be borne in mind that there has been a substantial increase in the number of canneries, together with longer seasons of constant operation, and an increased amount of fishing gear operating. . . . Formerly, the canneries fished only a few of the more important streams with traps, within a short distance of their stations. It is safe to say that there is not now a stream that salmon ascend that is not being fished to some extent. . . . There are now but few canneries, if any, that obtain all their salmon within a 100 mile radius; a great many of them regularly carry a large percentage of their fish 150 miles and some even go much farther for their fish. . . .

In the end the statistics will undoubtedly show the maximum capacity of production of salmon in Alaska, but it is feared that ere this is shown

[33] *Ibid.*, 1916, p. 386.

the supply will have become so badly depleted that the industry will have been ruined years before even the most drastic measures can recoup the losses and bring back the maximum production, if, in fact, it can ever be accomplished. There is conclusive evidence even now of the serious depletion of the salmon. It is a matter of common knowledge to practically all those residents of Alaska who have given the matter careful attention, . . . and many people who have had ample opportunity for observation, from the most illiterate native to the trained fishing expert and scholarly observer, bear testimony to the general truth of the statements herein set forth.[34]

Out of these conditions there developed an intense two-pronged effort on the part of the residents of Alaska to gain control over the management of the resource and to outlaw the use of traps which, because of their efficiency and pattern of ownership, had become the chief symbol for all the real and alleged evils of the absentee economic system under which the resource was being exploited. The Alaska packers saw this move on the part of the residents as a major threat. They quickly organized resistance to any legislation that would change the status quo.

For example, when Congress was considering a new organic act to replace the unworkable Act of 1884, to provide greater home rule for Alaska through the creation of a territorial legislature, the bill contained a provision allowing the territory to regulate and tax the fisheries. This was a power Congress had given to all preceding territories, and it was assumed by the residents that Alaska would be no exception. However, at the instigation of the canned-salmon industry an amendment was adopted on the floor of the Senate barring the territory of Alaska from any control over its fisheries and the bill became law in that form. The newly created territorial legislature was also greatly limited in other spheres which historically had been considered purely local matters.[35]

In the following months an editorial appeared in the industry trade journal explaining that the salmon canners had been worried that Alaska might gain concurrent powers to regulate and tax the fisheries, but that through the canners' diligent opposition "the

---

[34] *Ibid.*, pp. 386-389.

[35] 37 Stat. 512. A review of the history of this bill is presented in: U.S. Congress, House, Committee on Merchant Marine and Fisheries, *Alaska Fisheries, Hearings on H.R. 9528*, 64th Cong., 1st Sess., 1916, pp. 229 ff.

teeth of the measure have been pulled and the government has simply given Alaska a toy legislature to play politics with."[36] It was concluded triumphantly that "federal control and supervision of the fisheries will be continued as at present."

The Bureau of Fisheries was also opposed to any measure that would curb its powers in Alaska. E. Lester Jones, the Deputy Commissioner of Fisheries, wrote that the situation in Alaska called for full federal control allowing no division of responsibility with the territorial government. He said the contention in Alaska that the territory could better determine its own fishery affairs was susceptible of adverse criticism because of the strife and friction that would almost invariably follow such efforts to handle the situation, and that the present impartial and honestly administered program of the bureau would be more beneficial to all interests concerned. He concluded:

> Owing to the vast amount of pratical and scientific knowledge and information acquired and developed during an extended period by men of unusual training and experience in the Bureau of Fisheries, . . . any idea of transferring jurisdiction to the Territory or any other agency should be completely dismissed.[37]

When the territory's right to tax the fisheries was being contested in the federal courts by the salmon packers in 1915, Secretary of Commerce William C. Redfield wrote in his annual report:

> Clearly if the Territory of Alaska has a joint right of control over the whole or any part of such fisheries, the plans of the Department of Commerce for their growth and development may meet with serious interference and the result may be harmful to the industry. If, for example, the Legislature of Alaska may impose license fees and taxes to an extent that might seriously impair the industry by making it unprofitable, the Department of Commerce, charged with the responsibility of caring for the industry, would be practically helpless. . . . Not even the possibility of such a situation, much less the situation itself, should be allowed to exist.[38]

---

[36] *Pacific Fisherman,* September 1912, p. 16. (Ironically, many of the larger packers who were stanchly supporting federal control of the fisheries of Alaska were at the same time providing the main opposition to a current proposal to extend federal control over salmon fisheries in the coastal states. Obviously, it was not the principle of the thing but the desire to maintain the status quo that led them to this anomalous position.)

[37] *Ibid.,* January 1915, p. 11.

[38] U.S. Department of Commerce, *Annual Report of the Secretary of Commerce, 1915* (Washington: U.S. Government Printing Office, 1915), p. 117.

Thus, as the movement for home rule gained momentum, the industry and the bureau found themselves with a common cause—to keep the territory from regulating and controlling the fisheries. For each a vital interest was at stake.

As the conflict over the use of traps grew, the packers again had the full support of the bureau. The trap has already been discussed in a previous chapter and it will not be necessary to go into detail about the origin of the conflict. Although traps were frequently opposed on such grounds as their alleged ability to destroy entire runs of salmon, their wastefulness and their destruction of other species, the real reason for conflict was more basic. It was essentially a dispute between capital and labor. Traps were a costly form of gear beyond the means of the ordinary fisherman. Their ownership tended to fall into the hands of the packers or others closely affiliated with them. Through control of traps the packers could render themselves largely independent of the fishermen and thus keep down the price of raw fish while at the same time assuring themselves an adequate supply. A major fishermen's strike in southeast Alaska in 1912 revealed to the cannerymen the disadvantage of depending too heavily upon fishermen with mobile gear, and the high prices demanded by the strikers led to the adoption of traps in still greater numbers.

As a growing number of fishermen and laborers settled permanently in Alaska, this conflict developed into a major dispute between residents and nonresidents. The residents, backed in part by certain nonresident fishermen, maintained that the salmon fishery should be developed to encourage the settlement of Alaska by independent and self-supporting people. They feared that the existence and rapid extension in the use of company-owned traps was leading to a monopoly of the supply of fish by what was referred to locally as the "Fish Trust." This led to an insistence on the complete abolition of traps as the only logical solution to the conflict.

The Alaska packers, on the other hand, maintained that the sweeping abolition of their most economical form of gear would be confiscatory and ruinous to an industry having millions of dollars invested. Said the trade journal in 1913, "The fish trap is the best and only friend the canners have in Alaska, and if this method of catching fish is prohibited it will mean almost the entire dissolution of the salmon industry. . . ."[39] The canners sought not only to prevent any curtailment, but also to obtain the passage of legislation that would give trap ownership firmer legal sanction. As mentioned earlier, trap sites were acquired and held on a tenuous user-rights basis that was maintained only through a gentlemen's agreement to respect priority of use.

The bureau ignored the social and economic implications of the trap issue and in so doing aligned itself again with the packers. The chief of the Alaska division of the bureau wrote in 1913 that curtailment of traps would be tampering with the competitive system on which the economy was based and that " . . . as in other industries, competition when conducted legitimately, invariably inures to the public good." He pointed out that from the bureau's viewpoint the only factor in considering any fishing gear was its susceptibility to regulation. Since traps were stationary they could be inspected and regulated more easily and hence were ". . . more desirable in the interests of the fish supply."[40]

The bureau's alignment with the Alaska salmon packers on these various issues had a significant social impact within the territory. The residents saw themselves pitted in a one-sided battle against two mammoth forces—absentee capitalists and absentee government—neither of which seemed to have the welfare of the territory in mind. The continued existence of company-owned traps sanctioned by the bureau led to disrespect and disregard for the fishery laws and regulations, and it eventually bred a lawless attempt by certain elements within the territory to take matters into their own hands in what commonly became known as "trap piracy." The robbery of fish from traps had occurred in the past, but beginning in 1918 the problem grew to major dimensions owing to the high fish prices and a growing scarcity of fish. By 1919 it had reached alarming dimensions. Many traps were robbed in broad daylight, and rifle shots were exchanged between the robbers and the trap watchmen.

Appeals for help were sent to the Secretary of Commerce, and at his request the Navy Department dispatched the gunboat *Marblehead* and a subchaser to Alaska with instructions to coop-

---

[39] *Pacific Fisherman,* 1913, p. 15.

[40] U.S. Department of Commerce, Bureau of Fisheries, *Alaska Fisheries and Fur Seal Industries, 1913* (Washington: U.S. Government Printing Office, 1914), p. 45.

erate in the suppression of such piracy.[41] By 1920 two Navy subchasers, five Coast Guard vessels, four Coast and Geodetic vessels, and other boats of the Forest Service, Treasury Department, and Commerce Department were cooperating in fishery patrols to protect the traps from fish pirates. The canners also employed guards in large numbers to protect their property. In spite of these concerted efforts, piratical operations worsened in the years following. Although it was frequently pointed out that such unlawful activities could easily be prevented by the cannerymen themselves merely through their refusal to purchase salmon from suspicious sources, the competitive atmosphere was not conducive to such an agreement and the robbers continued to find a ready market for stolen fish.[42]

Every attempt to get through Congress additional legislation to enlarge the powers of the Secretary of Commerce to protect and conserve the Alaska salmon resource became entangled with these controversial issues. A few examples will illustrate the point.

In 1912 a bill to extend the authority of the Secretary for the regulation of the Alaska fishery was introduced in the Senate.[43] The bill proposed to allow the Secretary to prohibit fishing in any of the waters of Alaska under the jurisdiction of the United States, and it contained provisions that would: (1) increase the tax on the fishery, (2) increase the standards of efficiency and productiveness required of private hatcheries receiving tax rebates, (3) establish preferential rights to trap sites for existing owners, and (4) increase the distance of traps from the mouths of streams. Except for the provision giving preferential rights to trap sites, the proposed changes were emphatically opposed by the representatives of the canned-salmon industry. Both the Governor of Alaska and the congressional delegate vigorously opposed the trap provision, but otherwise supported the bill. Extensive hearings were held by the Senate Committee on Fisheries, but the bill never got out of committee.[44]

In 1913 the bureau drew up a tentative draft of a new bill

---

[41] *Pacific Fisherman,* August 1919, p. 30.

[42] U.S. Department of Commerce, Bureau of Fisheries, *Alaska Fishery and Fur-Seal Industries in 1920* (Washington: U.S. Government Printing Office, 1921), p. 30.

[43] S. 5856, 62nd Cong., 2nd Sess.

[44] U.S. Congress, Senate, Committee on Fisheries, *Alaska Fisheries, Hearings . . . on S. 5856,* 62nd Cong., 2nd Sess., 1912, 2 Vols., pp. 36, 563.

and circulated it to representatives of the canned-salmon industry. The First Territorial Legislature was in session at the time, and through an official representative the bureau urged the legislature to memorialize Congress to pass the bill.[45] However, the draft still contained the objectionable trap provision, and the territorial legislature chose instead to send a memorial to Congress strongly opposing this aspect of the bill. It was noted in the memorial that "it is the first step in taking over the ownership of the fisheries of Alaska by the great cannery interests. . . . It is the longed-for legal basis for the monopoly of the Alaska fisheries."[46]

Early in 1914 the bureau sent Deputy Commissioner of Fisheries E. Lester Jones to Alaska to investigate the fishery and to make recommendations as to legislative needs. It was decided that no further action would be taken on the tentative draft until his report was completed.[47]

As a countermove, the Alaska congressional delegate, James Wickersham, introduced a bill in the House for the conservation of the Alaska fisheries which contained a provision abolishing traps completely, but the bill never got out of committee.[48]

The bureau had another bill introduced in the House early in 1915 which was based on the recommendations of the Deputy Commissioner of Fisheries after his extended study of the situation in Alaska.[49] The bill proved to be only a slight modification of the earlier tentative draft which had been approved by the canned-salmon industry, and it contained the highly controversial provision granting preferential rights to traps. Its introduction led to a scathing attack of the bureau and the "Fish Trust" on the floor of the House by James Wickersham, Alaska's congressional delegate.[50] He charged that the bill was the culmination of the efforts of the Fish Trust to secure a complete monopoly of the Alaska fisheries.

> Unless Congress shall stop, look and listen, and know something about the fisheries situation in Alaska, the Swift Meat Trust, the Booth Fisheries Co., and the Alaska Packers Association, will own, as well

[45] *Pacific Fisherman,* May 1913, p. 14.
[46] U.S. *Congressional Record,* 63rd Cong., 3rd Sess., p. 702.
[47] *Pacific Fisherman,* April 1914, p. 19.
[48] H.R. 18144, 63rd Cong., 2nd Sess.
[49] H.R. 21607, 63rd Cong., 3rd Sess.
[50] U.S. *Congressional Record,* 63rd Cong., 3rd Sess., pp. 698-708.

as control, the immense food supply of Alaska under their trust arrangement and this bill.[51]

The delegates sent a lengthy letter to the President of the United States charging that the social and official intimacy existing between the industry and the bureau was becoming a public scandal and that over 200 million dollars worth of salmon had been extracted from the territory by the corporate interests "almost without law and quite without aid to the development of Alaska."[52] He concluded that only the powers of the President could break the hold of the Fish Trust over fishery officials, fishing legislation, and the fisheries of Alaska.

No action was taken on the bill, but in the next session another measure was prepared and introduced at the behest of the bureau.[53] The bill went even further in opposition to the views of the territorial interests and it was bitterly opposed by them. Unlike earlier bills, this one contained no provision to extend the powers of the Secretary to control and prohibit fishing beyond the narrow limits provided in the 1906 Act (i.e., 500 yards from the mouth of any stream). Such proposals had drawn heavy fire from the canned-salmon industry in the past. Two provisions were particularly controversial. One would prohibit territorial taxation of the fisheries in any form, and the tax laws already enacted by the Territorial Legislature were to be repealed. A new federal tax schedule was provided which would for the first time place a tax on the fishermen's catch, at the same time reducing the tax on the canned product. The other controversial provision granted definite exclusive fishing rights to traps, and these could be mortgaged, transferred, or sold by the owners like any other property. The bill went much further than any previous attempt to grant perpetual and exclusive rights to trap sites.

Among other less controversial provisions, it was proposed that all privately owned hatcheries would be purchased by the federal government. The only section of the bill that could be considered a restrictive measure provided certain additional limits on how close traps could be placed to each other and on the length of the lead between the trap and the shoreline. However, even

[51] *Ibid.*, p. 700.
[52] *Ibid.*, p. 700.
[33] H.R. 9528, 64th Cong., 1st Sess.

these provisions had advantages for the trap owner, who would thus have a larger area of water under his exclusive control.

Extensive hearings were held and top government officials, including Secretary of Commerce Redfield, appeared along with representatives of the canned-salmon industry to support the bill in all its provisions.[54] The bill was reported favorably out of committee, but in the debate on the floor of the House James Wickersham, the Alaska delegate, made a strong last-ditch stand which proved successful in preventing the bill from coming to a vote before adjournment of the session.[55] The delegate pleaded that everything good in the bill was already in the law and that the tax provision would leave Alaska with no source of income of its own. To the delegate, the greatest evil was the provision granting exclusive fishing rights to the trap owner for about 320 acres around each trap. Since there was no limit on the number of these sites a company or corporation could own, the real effect of the bill, he said, would be to give a monopoly of the control and ownership of the Alaska fisheries to three great corporations.[56]

Bills continued to be introduced in each session of Congress "for the protection and conservation of the Alaska fisheries," but for one reason or another they drew sufficient opposition from the interest groups to prevent their passage. As prices of canned salmon soared during the war, the intensity of fishing and canning operations rose to new heights with little interference from the federal government.

The factor most responsible for causing a break in the legislative stalemate was the collapse of the markets for canned salmon immediately following World War I. The tremendous increase in production during the war had occurred primarily in the lower grade pink and chum species, which previously had been canned only on a small scale. With the ending of large military purchases in 1919, an abrupt decrease in demand occurred that left the packers and brokers with a heavy surplus of these species. There were no alternative established markets. Stocks of salmon were

[54] U.S. Congress, House, Committee on Merchant Marine and Fisheries, *Alaska Fisheries, Hearing on H.R. 9526,* 64th Cong., 1st Sess., 1916, pp. 396.

[55] U.S. *Congressional Record,* 64th Cong., 1st Sess., p. 13374.

[56] *Ibid.,* 64th Cong., 2nd Sess., pp. 288-289, 309.

further increased by the return of large military surpluses which also had to be disposed of on the domestic market. Export markets were greatly restricted by the adverse rate of exchange that developed, and this was made worse by the successful entrance into certain world markets of the Oriental salmon pack from Japanese canneries in Siberia. In addition, during the war costs of production had risen to the highest on record, and they remained high in the years following.

The market failure caused great anxiety among the packers, who had become accustomed to disposing of their output early in the season at high prices. It led to temporary consolidations and other vigorous efforts to cut costs and reduce output. By 1920 the packers were offering to sell at prices considerably below the costs of production, but were still unable to move the pack.[57]

The necessity to curtail production for economic reasons, and the recognition that this could not be accomplished solely on a voluntary basis under the competitive conditions that existed, induced an immediate and phenomenal change in the attitude of the salmon packers toward "conservation" of the resource. It was reported in the trade journal that the disastrous canning season of 1919 "had the salutary effect of awakening the canning interests to the strong possibility of the industry being on the downgrade." In November of that year the cannerymen approached both federal and territorial authorities with a proposition for the appointment of a joint committee to prepare a comprehensive bill "that would assure a greater escapement of salmon to the spawning beds."[58] At the annual convention of the Association of Pacific Fisheries in 1920, the business session was devoted primarily to a discussion of the "opportunities offered by the present unavoidable period of contraction for the initiation of suitable measures to conserve and replenish the salmon fisheries."[59]

Salmon canners who until this time had vehemently denied that the resource was being depleted now were willing to admit the point. The principal speaker at the 1920 salmon-can-

---

[57] *Pacific Fisherman,* September 1920, p. 21.
[58] *Ibid.,* February 1920, p. 23.
[59] *Ibid.,* December 1920, p. 21.

ners convention was Frank M. Warren, president of the Alaska Portland Packers Association, one of the largest canning concerns in Alaska. Mr. Warren told the packers:

> We have been overfishing the country generally; there is no doubt about that, and one main essential that we have to consider . . . is whether we have borrowed from the future, and whether we are going to get the packs of salmon in the future that we have had in the past.[60]

With respect to the poor marketing conditions, Mr. Warren said:

> I think you ought to consider this condition as a blessing in disguise, and if it does not do anything else than force a curtailment of the pack which will result in the better seeding of the spawning grounds throughout the territory, . . . we will be in better condition in the long run than any of us ever dreamed of. . . . So, altogether, it seems to me that the cloud has a mighty bright lining to it.[61]

E. B. Deming, head of Pacific American Fisheries Company, also one of the largest in Alaska, doubted if his company would be able to operate at all the next year. He suggested that until the law of supply and demand began correcting the present market conditions "we should devote our efforts and our thoughts toward the conservation of the fish."[62]

In search of someone other than themselves to blame for the condition of the fishery, the canners trained their guns for the first time on the Bureau of Fisheries. Dr. Hugh Smith, the Commissioner of Fisheries since 1913 who had been praised so highly by the cannerymen over the years, became the scapegoat, and he was subjected to a vehement attack which began in March of 1921. President Harding had just entered office, and Herbert Hoover had been appointed to the position of Secretary of Commerce in the new administration. The industry trade journal reported that Hoover had expressed a keen interest in building closer relations with the leading fishery operators in the development of the commercial fisheries. The editor concluded that Secretary Hoover's preliminary statements "would seem to justify the hope that, under Hoover's guidance, the Bureau will emerge from the academic atmosphere that has often surrounded it, and

---

[60] *Ibid.*, p. 21.
[61] *Ibid.*, p. 21.
[62] *Ibid.*, p. 21.

engage itself more actively and energetically in building up the industry."[63] Two months later, in a long editorial diatribe entitled "Is This Incompetence or What?" Dr. Smith was attacked for his "habit of bungling."[64] In September the journal said that when Dr. Smith had been appointed in 1913 it was hoped that the bureau might take the guiding position in the constructive conservation of the Alaska fisheries, but "the result . . . has been most disappointing; and after eight years of inaction, blundering and failure, the conclusion is inevitable that, in his whole attitude and mental calibre, Dr. Smith is unfitted to administer an office of this kind."[65]

Although the trade journal had expressed fears in 1913 that Dr. Smith might make the bureau "too scientific," Smith was now accused of neglecting necessary studies to obtain definite information on the habits and life history of the salmon.[66] While the canners had insisted at congressional hearings and elsewhere, year after year, that no depletion was occurring, the trade journal now concluded that "even before Dr. Smith took office, the approaching danger to the salmon fishery and the need of accurate knowledge were apparent to anyone interested in its future. . . ."[67] Finally, of the bureau policies which the canned-salmon industry had been so instrumental in shaping, it was charged that in the eight years of Dr. Smith's direction

> there has been no manifestation of definite or consistent conservation policy toward the Alaska salmon fishery. . . . During the entire period the fishery has been passing through a critical condition, but such steps toward conservation as have been taken have usually been faltering and ineffective. In this the commissioner's position has been that of a reluctant follower rather than a leader, waiting until driven to action by obvious necessity, rather than foreseeing and forestalling conditions as one really interested in the fishery would have done.[68]

A few months later Dr. Smith resigned under a cloud of suspicion after nearly thirty-five years with the bureau. Henry O'Malley, who had been in charge of the Pacific coast activities

---

[63] *Ibid.*, March 1921, p. 35.
[64] *Ibid.*, May 1921, p. 21.
[65] *Ibid.*, September 1921, p. 18.
[66] *Ibid.*, p. 18.
[67] *Ibid.*, p. 18.
[68] *Ibid.*, p. 18.

of the bureau since 1918, was appointed commissioner, and the new appointment was received enthusiastically by the Alaska cannerymen.[69]

Dr. C. H. Gilbert, professor of zoology at Stanford University, who over the years had been employed on a number of occasions by the bureau to undertake special investigations of the Alaska fisheries, summed up the situation late in 1921:

> Up until the present I have never known cannerymen operating in Alaska to come forward in any number publicly and state that Alaska was being overfished and that the salmon supply was in danger. . . . You can go along the entire coast of Alaska and talk with those engaged in fishing in past years, and you will not find any man . . . who does not admit that the salmon supply has been seriously impaired and that the end of the industry is in sight in the not very distant future unless some strenuous measures are taken.[70]

Secretary Hoover and the new Commissioner of Fisheries recognized the seriousness of the situation and immediately tried to gain passage of legislation to extend federal jurisdiction and authority so that adequate regulations could be promulgated.

The stage appeared to be perfectly set. All the major interest groups were in agreement that the resource was being seriously depleted and that it was absolutely necessary to have further controls and restrictions if the trend was to be reversed. Nevertheless, differences of opinion over the means to be used continued to stymie all efforts to obtain a compromise on a particular bill, just as had happened under previous administrations.

The bureau found itself in the unenviable position of being criticized from all sides for allowing depletion of the resource to continue almost unchecked, yet it was without the power to act further and unable to gain congressional approval for the extension of its authority. There was even talk that the fisheries functions should be transferred from the Department of Commerce to the Department of Agriculture.[71]

Faced with these conditions, Secretary Hoover became convinced that the situation called for immediate action. He prevailed upon

---

[69] *Ibid.*, June 1922, p. 17.

[70] U.S. Congress, House, Merchant Marine and Fisheries Committee, *Fisheries in Alaska, Hearings on H.R. 2394,* 67th Cong., 1st Sess., 1921, p. 46.

[71] *Pacific Fisherman,* April 1922, p. 18.

President Harding to promulgate emergency measures by Executive Order, and this resulted in what became known as the "reservation policy." It is the most revolutionary and controversial move ever attempted in the management of the Alaska salmon fishery, for it represents the only attempt in the history of the commercial fishery to deviate from the principle of a free and common fishery. It has so many important implications for the purposes of this study that it is desirable to trace the development of the policy in some detail.

As will be recalled, a number of proposals had been made in earlier years to adopt one or another system of licensing and leasing of fishing rights (i.e., of canneries or gear, or both) to control the *amount* of fishing effort as an alternative to the existing system which allowed free entry into the fishery. None of these was given serious consideration primarily because each represented a radical departure from the existing methods of regulation, and there was strong resistance from nearly all elements in the fishery, including the regulating agency, to any change in the status quo. Then in 1919 Dr. C. H. Gilbert and Henry O'Malley undertook a special investigation of the Alaska salmon resource for the bureau, which resulted in one of the most forthright and penetrating reports ever completed on the problems of the fishery.[72] The idea behind the reservation policy undoubtedly germinated from the conclusions of this study, for the policy was adopted shortly after Henry O'Malley was appointed Commissioner of Fisheries and it bore close resemblance to what he and Dr. Gilbert had recommended.

It was stated candidly in the report that the problems of conserving the salmon resource could not be understood and approached rationally without taking into consideration basic economic motivations. The present administration of the resource, it was pointed out, was based on the expectation that men would hold back when further profits could be made, but this was witless since no administration of public affairs could depend on men voluntarily forgoing a profit. It was noted that as long as the public threw the fishery open to unrestricted competition,

[72] C. H. Gilbert and Henry O'Malley, "Special Investigation of the Salmon Fishery in Central and Western Alaska," *Alaska Fisheries and Fur Seal Industries in 1919*, U.S. Bureau of Fisheries (Washington: U.S. Government Printing Office, 1920), pp. 143-160.

and as long as there was keen rivalry for every fish that swam, no individual canner or fisherman could voluntarily accomplish anything toward protection of the streams.

> Whatever the individual canner spared for spawning purposes, his competitors would thankfully accept and place in cans. He is powerless to conserve either the public interest, or even—should he be sufficiently enlightened to see it—his own private interest, by listening to any counsel of moderation.[73]

It was the authors' belief that if fishing grounds or fishing rights could be leased or assigned, and property rights acquired which would become valueless should the fishing greatly decline, co-operation with the authorities to preserve the resource could be confidently counted on.

> But so long as the present policy is maintained, and the canners have only what they can seize and hold with every man's hand against them, there can be but one final outcome. Total exhaustion of the fisheries will occur; if not tomorrow, then the day after.[74]

Finally it was concluded:

> The dangers which confront the Alaska salmon industry are inherent in the very plan which the Congress has adopted for its administration. The only effective remedy lies in altering the groundwork of this plan, in treating the fisheries resources in practice as well as theory as the property of the public, and in administering them in the interests of the public rather than apparently in the interests of those who seek to exploit them.[75]

These conclusions were followed by a series of specific recommendations to assure the permanency of the resource while still leaving fishery operations in private hands. Canneries were to be treated as exercising quasi-public functions, and would be licensed to operate within restricted limits on a specific scale with a given amount of gear which could not be modified without direct authorization. No more canneries would be allowed to operate in a given area than could do so while still maintaining the runs at their maximum production. Expansion would be permitted only when evidence showed this could be safely done. Output of the canneries would be restricted whenever the danger point approached in a particular area, and a safety factor

[73] *Ibid.*, p. 287.
[74] *Ibid.*, 287.
[75] *Ibid.*, p. 287.

would be maintained at all times in favor of the spawning beds. When conditions permitted a degree of expansion of operations, the equity of existing operators would be recognized.

Under these conditions, it was concluded, the packers would cooperate with the government because it would be to their interests and those of the public to conserve the runs of salmon. Also, the difficulties of enforcing the law would be greatly simplified. Finally, it was stated that however notorious such a plan might have been during the industry's infancy, under present conditions it would be wholly impractical to continue arguing the point.[76]

In 1921 Secretary Hoover began to realize the difficulties he faced in getting additional legislation through Congress to extend his powers. He invited all parties interested in the fishery to attend a conference in Washington, D. C. in the hope that some compromise measure could be agreed upon. The Alaska salmon packers held a preliminary meeting in Seattle prior to the conference to discuss what measures would be supported or opposed, and among the ideas discussed was a suggestion that the Alaska salmon fishery be placed in a reservation and that the number of canneries and the amount of gear be controlled through a system of licensing.[77] While the canners had opposed such proposals in the past, the idea now seemed appealing. For one thing, it was possible that under such a system traps would be given property rights, thus ending the controversy over their status. For another thing, a number of large Eastern concerns had been showing an interest in expanding into the salmon-canning business in Alaska, and it was felt that such a system would prevent their entry unless they were willing to purchase existing canneries and equipment. The canners gave their general endorsement to the reservation idea at the meeting, but they concluded that the subject was of such a controversial nature that it would undoubtedly be a waste of time and effort to urge such a plan.[78]

---

[76] *Ibid.*, pp. 287-288. (With respect to fishing gear and fishing sites, it was proposed that sites be licensed and that property rights vest in them under prescribed regulation. The nature and amount of gear would be specified in each cannery license. Unless certain conditions were met these locations would revert to the public; otherwise they would be the property of the licensee so long as they could be operated without detriment to the salmon supply.)

[77] *Pacific Fisherman*, October 1921, p. 16.

[78] *Ibid.*, p. 16.

At the Hoover conference in October there was general agreement among the interests and the government that legislation to extend the powers of the Secretary was badly needed; but conflict again developed between packers, territorial representatives, and labor groups over the specific form the legislation should take. When it became clear to Secretary Hoover that there was little chance for agreement, he warned that unless an Act was passed in the current session of Congress to extend his authority, it might be necessary to adopt emergency measures to prevent the continuing depletion of the resource.[79]

When in fact no legislation was passed during that session, the Secretary decided to act. Armed with the knowledge that his decision would be supported by the salmon packers, Hoover requested the President to create an Alaska Peninsula Fishery Reserve, and on February 17, 1922, President Harding proclaimed by Executive Order the establishment of the first such reserve ever to be created in the United States.[80] It was presumed that the President had the authority to create such reserves under the General Withdrawal Act of 1910, which allowed the President to withdraw lands from the public domain and to reserve such lands for various public purposes.[81] In July Hoover warned that other reserves would be established to cover other fishing areas in Alaska unless Congress acted immediately.[82] When no further action was taken, the Southwestern Alaska Fishery Reservation, including the important Bristol Bay and Kodiak areas, was similarly created in November 1922. These two reserves took in about 40 per cent of the fishing grounds of Alaska.

No person was allowed to engage in fishing, canning, or preparing salmon within the reserves without first obtaining a permit from the Secretary of Commerce. Applications for permits, stating the size and location of the proposed operation, had to be presented to the Secretary prior to January 15 of each year. When a permit was issued, it specified precisely the size of the

---

[79] *Ibid.*, November 1921, p. 7.

[80] U.S. Department of Commerce, *Annual Report of the Secretary of Commerce, 1922* (Washington: U.S. Government Printing Office, 1923), p. 172.

[81] A discussion of the legal aspects as seen by the solicitor of the Department of Commerce is discussed in: U.S. Congress, House, Merchant Marine and Fisheries Committee, *Fisheries of Alaska, Hearings on H.R. 2714,* 68th Cong., 1st Sess., 1924, p. 118ff.

[82] *Pacific Fisherman,* July 1922, p. 7.

pack that could be put up and the character and extent of fishing operations allowed. Each reserve was subdivided into a number of smaller areas and the permits were valid in only one area for one year. Transportation of fish between areas was not permitted. During the first year, permits could be issued only to individuals and concerns already operating in the reserves.[83]

The reservation policy was enthusiastically received by the canned-salmon industry. The trade journal called the policy the wisest and most constructive step ever taken to preserve the Alaska salmon fisheries.[84] At the annual convention of the Association of Pacific Fisheries a resolution was passed unanimously supporting the policy, and a committee of packers was appointed to press Secretary Hoover to extend the reserves to other fishing grounds in Alaska.[85] The potent U.S. Fisheries Association with which the Alaska salmon canners had become closely aligned through their own associations, passed a resolution at its annual meeting endorsing the reserves and calling for their immediate extension. Copies of the resolution were sent to the President of the United States, the Secretary of Commerce, the Commissioner of Fisheries, members of Congress, and other government officials.[86]

Early in 1923 market conditions began to improve slightly, and new concern developed among the salmon packers lest these conditions attract Eastern operators who, it was rumored, were waiting for the right opportunity to move into the Alaska fishery. An emergency meeting of the salmon packers was called to consider the situation. As a result of the meeting the packers went on record unanimously in favor of the immediate establishment of a third reservation to include all the waters of Alaska not already with the boundaries of the two reserves.[87]

The Alaska reaction to the reserves was at first divided, but as

[83] U.S. Department of Commerce, Bureau of Fisheries, *Report of the U.S. Commissioner of Fisheries, 1922*, Document No. 913 (Washington: U.S. Government Printing Office, 1923), pp. 39-42.

[84] *Pacific Fisherman*, September 1922, p. 20.

[85] *Ibid.*, December 1922, p. 15.

[86] *Ibid.*, October 1922, p. 9. (The U.S. Fisheries Association was more or less an association of all major fishing interests in the United States; an association of associations, so to speak. It was later superseded by the National Fisheries Association. Both provided an extremely effective lobby organization in Washington, D. C.).

[87] *Ibid.*, January 1923, pp. 14-15.

administration under the new policy got under way an impassioned opposition developed. At hearings in Seattle concerning regulations under the reserves, Alaska's congressional delegate, Dan Sutherland, spoke in objection to what he termed the parceling out of five thousand miles of Alaska's coastline to a few individuals without the territory's having a voice in it. He characterized the reservation system as un-American, outrageous, and intended to create monopoly. He declared his intention of fighting the reserves in Congress, and he was confident that when sufficient information was presented on the effects of the reserves the system would be overthrown.[88]

Early in 1923, Delegate Sutherland launched his attack from the floor of the House. He charged that no notice of the intention to create the reserves was given to the people most vitally concerned—the coastal people of Alaska—nor to their representative in Congress, nor to the general public, "but was accomplished surreptitiously at the instigation of the packers' attorneys who came to Washington, D. C., early in 1922 to push the idea through. . . ."[89] He pointed out that under the system of licensing provided, each cannery was alloted a certain number of boats, and the only way a fisherman could operate was to become a tenant of the cannerymen who held the license. He concluded that in earlier years when forest reserves were created by Executive Order under Presidents Roosevelt and Taft, the action had been taken primarily to prevent a monopoly in public resources, but in the present case of the Alaska salmon resource

> the sole purpose in the minds of those who originated the proposition was the granting of a monopoly to the red salmon trust. The proposition was conceived and engineered to completion by the Fish Trust, and now the Department of Commerce hypocritically pretends that it was projected in the interest of conservation. . . . Congress has refused to act in the past . . . and while Congress holds aloof the Fish Trust secures full control of our natural food supply upon which the people of the Territory depend more than upon any other resource for a livelihood.[90]

In 1923 Alaska received more close personal attention from high federal officials than it had ever had before. Assistant Secretary of

[88] *Ibid.*, December 1922, p. 14.
[89] U.S. *Congressional Record,* 67th Cong., 4th Sess., p. 4942.
[90] *Ibid.*, p. 4942.

Commerce C. H. Huston went to Alaska with a party of officials from the Bureau of Fisheries to make certain essential inquiries regarding the fisheries of Alaska and other important matters. Conferences were held with Governor Bone and other local officials, and particular emphasis was given to discussion of measures to perpetuate the salmon supply.[91] Late in the spring a large congressional delegation sailed north to look into certain matters in Alaska. Accompanying them was Dr. C. H. Gilbert, who had been employed by the Bureau of Fisheries to administer the fishery reserves.[92] In August Senator Wesley Jones and Representative L. H. Hadley of the state of Washington toured Alaska on an inspection trip to obtain information "for use in shaping future legislation and determining policies in respect to the administration of the fisheries in Alaska."[93] With them was the Commissioner of Fisheries, Henry O'Malley.

The most notable event, however, was the visit during July of President Harding, who was accompanied by Secretary of Commerce Herbert Hoover, Secretary of Agriculture Henry C. Wallace, Secretary of the Interior Hubert Work, Speaker of the House Frederick H. Gillet, and other prominent men from Washington, D. C. The group made an extended tour of the territory and inquired into the workings of various federal agencies. Secretary Hoover personally conducted public hearings at Juneau, Cordova, Seward, Nenana, Anchorage, and Fairbanks to "secure first hand information in regard to fishery conditions in Alaska."[94]

In his speech in Seattle at the end of the tour and just before his death, President Harding devoted considerable attention to the problems of the salmon fishery. What the President had seen and heard in Alaska thoroughly aroused him to the need for more effective restriction. Yet, he said, his earnest desire was to avoid unjust discrimination among the conflicting interests that had been clamoring for his attention. Said the President:

---

[91] U.S. Department of Commerce, Bureau of Fisheries, *Alaska Fisheries and Fur-Seal Industries in 1922,* Document 951 (Washington: U.S. Government Printing Office, 1923), p. 3.

[92] U.S. Department of Commerce, Bureau of Fisheries, *Alaska Fisheries and Fur-Seal Industries in 1923,* Document 973 (Washington: U.S. Government Printing Office, 1925), p. 50.

[93] *Ibid.,* p. 50.

[94] *Ibid.,* pp. 48-49.

> Against any kind of prohibition, it is urged that the immense investments in Alaska's fisheries and canneries would be greatly injured by . . . a reduction in the catch. To this it may well be replied that the canneries would better have their catches reduced by Government regulation for a time than extermination in a few years through their own excesses. . . . If there is defiance, it is better to destroy the defiant investor than to demolish a national resource which needs only guarding against greed to remain a permanent asset of incalculable value.[95]

He called upon Congress to agree upon a program of equitable legislation, and he concluded:

> The processes of development and establishment of permanent and ample civilization lie in a citizenship with homes in Alaska, not in investors who are seeking Alaskan wealth to enrich homes elsewhere. . . . Against a program of ruinous exploitation we must stand firmly. Our adopted program must be development of Alaska for Alaskans. To plan for wise, well-rounded development into a permanent community of homes, families, schools and an illuminating social scheme, we must give all encouragement.
>
> . . . If, for example, we should go on decimating the fisheries year by year till they have been ruined, . . . then we shall never have a community of stabilized society and home-tied people.[96]

Secretary Hoover's speech followed the President's. He called for congressional action and warned again that in the meantime the administration did not intend to sit idly by denying responsibility, but would use the reservation authority to its fullest extent. He expressed no viewpoint toward the social and economic conditions in Alaska but concluded tersely: "Our only purpose is to restore salmon. . . . Pious statements, scientific discussion, and political oratory will not spawn salmon."[97] These statements, along with the other public notice Alaska received during the year, focused national attention on the condition of the salmon fishery and the need for immediate action by Congress.

It became clear in the latter part of 1923 that many salmon packers and government officials were no longer thinking of the reserves as temporary emergency measures. Speaking of legislative needs, the editor of the trade journal proclaimed that some such system as that followed by the Department of Commerce in

---

[95] *Pacific Fisherman,* August 1923, p. 7.
[96] *Ibid.,* p. 7.
[97] *Ibid.,* p. 7.

the new reserves seemed to be a necessity.[98] When Senator Jones returned from his trip to Alaska, he declared himself in favor of the reservation system and said he would urge that all of the territory be included.[99] Commissioner O'Malley, in a speech before the salmon canners on his return from Alaska, said that in regulating the salmon fishery the Bureau had three possible courses of action: first, to stand by while the fish were being destroyed; second, to grant permits to all comers with general restrictions sufficient to protect the fish but which would result in operations being reduced to a point of financial disaster; and third, to restrict the number of operators as well as the amount of gear used. He argued that the latter approach was the only rational way to regulate the fishery and that the reserves were the logical method to accomplish it.[100] Later he told the packers that the bureau planned to secure approval of Congress for the existing reservations and for authority to extend them where conditions warranted.[101] Secretary Hoover made the same recommendation in his annual report for 1923.[102]

With the convening of the Sixty-eighth Congress in December 1923, a series of bills was introduced representing the conflicting points of view on how the Alaska salmon resource should be managed and conserved. Two identical bills, S. 486 and H.R. 2714, introduced respectively by Senator Wesley L. Jones of Washington and Representative Wallace H. White, Jr., of Maine, specifically granted permission to the President to establish fishing reserves and make regulations governing fishing therein. Alaska's delegate to Congress, Dan Sutherland, wishing to get rid of the existing reserves and prevent establishment of others, introduced H.R. 4826 which gave the Secretary of Commerce full powers to regulate the fishery in all the territorial waters of Alaska, but provided that no exclusive right of fishery could be granted. The bill also contained a provision severely restricting the use of traps.[103] A similar bill, S. 188, was introduced in the Senate.[104]

---

[98] *Ibid.*, June 1923, p. 16.

[99] *Ibid.*, September 1923, p. 11.

[100] *Ibid.*, p. 11.

[101] *Ibid.*, December 1923, p. 14.

[102] U.S. Department of Commerce, *Annual Report of the Secretary of Commerce, 1923* (Washington: U.S. Government Printing Office, 1924) pp. 36-37.

[103] The trap provision barred granting of permanent trap privileges and forbade the use of traps in any bay, inlet or estuary less than three miles wide or within a mile of the mouth of any salmon stream.

[104] U.S. *Congressional Record*, 68th Cong., 1st Sess., pp. 85, 90, 104, 678.

The battle lines were drawn and action followed quickly. Resolutions were introduced in the House and Senate by Delegate Sutherland and Senator William H. King of Utah, respectively, calling for full congressional investigation of the Alaska fishery reserves and their administration by the Bureau of Fisheries. The resolutions called attention to various allegations made against the reserves, and complained of abuses both in the administration and in the conduct of the industry in general.[105] The territorial legislature transmitted a memorial to Congress deploring the indiscriminate creation of reserves. The memorialists concluded:

> A government of a reserve is essentially a government by men instead of by law and places the individual fortunes at the mercy of official whim. Irrespective of the good intentions of present officials, the privileges upon a reserve must, in the very nature of things, go to those who maintain the strongest lobby. It cannot be presumed that before the Bureau of Fisheries . . . a claimant who can neither appear in person nor by counsel can possibly have an even chance with one who is constantly represented by men specially skilled in presenting facts.[106]

Delegate Sutherland filed suit in the District of Columbia to enjoin the Secretary of Commerce from issuing permits for fishing in Alaskan waters, on the basis that the reserves were unconstitutional.[107]

The salmon packers met in Seattle in January of 1924 to mobilize their efforts. A motion was made and carried with only a few dissenting votes expressing approval of the two bills granting powers to establish permanent fishing reserves. It was noted that while the administration of the reserves might not be perfect, "under the old free-for-all, catch-as-catch-can, devil-take-the-hindmost system . . . the salmon fishery within a few years would be wiped out."[108]

In February, hearings were held by the Merchant Marine and Fisheries Committee in Washington, D. C. on H.R. 2714 to give the President full authority in establishing and regulating reserves. Appearing in support of the bill were: E. S. McCord, attorney and principal lobbyist for the canned-salmon industry; U.S. Commis-

[105] H. Res. 107 and S. Res. 58, 68th Cong., 1st Sess. See: *Ibid.*, pp. 229, 479, 7160, 9680.

[106] U.S. *Congressional Record,* 68th Cong., 1st Sess., p. 9688.

[107] *Pacific Fisherman,* January 1924, p. 5.

[108] *Ibid.*, p. 5.

sioner of Fisheries Henry O'Malley; the Solicitor of the Department of Commerce; and a number of individual salmon packers. In opposition along with Delegate Sutherland were three representatives of major West Coast labor unions.[109] The presentations were repetitive of the past.

Commissioner O'Malley pointed out that the legislation was needed because the reserves were being attacked in court, and if their validity should be destroyed the bureau would have nothing but the insignificant provisions of the 1906 Act to fall back on.[110] He was supported in this view by a letter from Secretary Hoover calling for immediate action before another of our national heritages was destroyed.[111] McCord presented a brief for the packers in which it was explained that if the bill became law

> it can be safely predicted that for all time the fisheries of Alaska will continue to furnish a valuable food supply to the Nation, will furnish employment for thousands of men, and will result in a great benefit not only to the men who have invested their money in the fishing industry, but the people of Alaska and the people of the Nation.[112]

Delegate Sutherland introduced voluminous documentary evidence to show the extent of opposition to the reserves in Alaska. He charged that the cannery interests supported the reservations because they could control the Department of Commerce and Bureau of Fisheries "if there were no law but only Department regulations." He cited evidence to show how the existing reserves had been administered to the great detriment of the local fishermen, especially in the letting of licenses to the larger packing concerns who were able to control who could and who could not fish.[113] He submitted a brief on fishery law to support his contention that the reserves were unconstitutional.[114]

The labor representatives charged that the bureau had not consided the effects upon the fishermen of the regulations for the

---

[109] U.S.Congress, House, Merchant Marine and Fisheries Committee, *Fisheries of Alaska, Hearings on H.R. 2714,* 68th Cong., 1st Sess., 1924, 346 pp. (The union representatives were: I.N. Hylen, Alaska Fisherman's Union; Edgar Wallace, American Federation of Labor; and Andrew Furuseth, President of the International Seaman's Union of America.)

[110] *Ibid.,* p. 19.

[111] *Ibid.,* pp. 246-248.

[112] *Ibid.,* p. 180.

[113] *Ibid.,* pp. 21-99.

[114] *Ibid.,* pp. 84-88, 123-136.

reserves. An example was cited where all fishing had been prohibited on the Karluk River except by two company-owned and operated weirs placed high in the river, and the canners in that area divided the catch from the weirs. This particular regulation was later rescinded when the bureau was reminded that weirs had been specifically outlawed in the 1889 Act, but the example was used to show the trend of thinking within the bureau. During the hearings, Delegate Sutherland asked the Commissioner if he would have continued to allow the weirs if they had not been illegal. The Commissioner replied that from a conservation standpoint it would have been highly desirable. "I was not thinking about the destruction of the labor situation, which seems to enter this thing. . . ."[115] This lack of concern over the problems of the fishermen led the labor representatives to oppose giving the bureau complete discretion in the setting of regulations as provided in the bill under consideration, but to prefer instead the passage of a much more detailed and rigid Act. Concluded one of the labor officials:

> The packers are in a position to call large meetings out on the Coast whenever they feel so inclined and, while I feel the Bureau of Fisheries means to do the right thing . . . they are constantly up against the "interests" and they are in a very ticklish position, and a position I would not care a great deal about being in myself; while if Congress set an iron-clad rule on certain things that could be done, the Commissioner would be removed from any temptation whatsoever.[116]

Attention was given the reservation bill in a number of major newspapers throughout the country, and the Hearst papers claimed that Secretary Hoover was turning over the Alaska salmon fisheries to a great corporation. The impact of these charges on Congress and the general public was heightened by the current debates in the Senate on the Teapot Dome oil-lease scandal.[117] Secretary Hoover found it advisable to defend himself and the administration, and the public debate that ensued tended to further publicize the

---

[115] *Ibid.*, pp. 272-274.

[116] *Ibid.*, p. 233.

[117] This scandal arose from the granting of leases in the Wyoming Naval Oil Reserves to private interests on unduly generous terms. A number of high government officials, including members of the Cabinet were accused of flagrant corruption in connection with the transactions and the leases were later cancelled by the Supreme Court.

seriousness of the situation in Alaska and the need for immediate congressional action.[118]

The House Merchant Marine and Fisheries Committee, to whom the reservation bill had been referred, was under pressure to act. However, the committee realized that conflict over the reservation bill was of sufficient intensity to prevent its passage, and so the bill was never reported out of committee. Instead, the committee drew up an entirely new bill, H.R. 8143, based on the various bills that had been introduced in both the House and Senate in the last few sessions. The compromise measure was introduced in the House on March 22, 1924, by Representative Wallace White of Maine, who was chairman of the committee.[119] The White bill, as it became known, was reported out of committee without amendment on March 24 and referred to the House with a unanimous recommendation that it pass.[120] The committee report accompanying the bill reviewed the history of unsuccessful attempts to get additional measures adopted for the conservation of the Alaska salmon. It concluded that some compromise measure must be adopted immediately if the salmon resource was to be saved and that H.R. 8143 offered a fair adjustment on the various conflicting issues.[121]

The most significant provision of the compromise proposal provided that the Secretary of Commerce would have full powers to limit or prohibit fishing in *all* the territorial waters of Alaska and that "all regulations authorized to be made shall be of general application and that no exclusive right of fishery shall be granted." This amounted to a very considerable extension in the jurisdiction and authority of the Secretary over that provided in the 1906 Act. It also meant a direct abrogation of the reservation policy and the concept behind it. The committee's stand on this was emphatically stated in the report to the House:

> At the present time it is the policy of the department . . . to grant a limited number of fishing permits within any designated area and to exclude all others from fishing therein. Your committee does not question the purpose of the department in this regard, but it has reached the

[118] *New York Times,* April 28, 1924, p. 3; and May 1, 1924, p. 20.

[119] U.S. *Congressional Record*, 68th Cong., 1st Sess., p. 4773.

[120] *Ibid.*, p. 4912.

[121] U.S. Congress, House, Merchant Marine and Fisheries Committee, *House Report 357 to accompany H.R. 8143,* 68th Cong., 1st Sess., March 24, 1924, p. 2.

unanimous and positive opinion that this practice of granting exclusive fishing privileges should cease.[122]

The bill also proposed that no fixed gear could be set in waters where the distance from shore to shore was less than one thousand feet, or within five hundred yards of any salmon stream. This represented a considerable extension over the 1906 Act which restricted such fishing only on red salmon streams less than 500 feet in width. Another provision amended the 1906 Act to enlarge the Secretary's authority to extend weekly closed periods with no exceptions, and it increased the severity of the penalties that could be imposed for violation of the law.

The bill was debated on the floor of the House on April 2. Representative Erwin L. Davis of Tennessee spoke in favor of immediate passage, noting that it was a compromise measure less drastic than some members of the committee thought it should be although others felt it went futher than it should. Nevertheless, he believed that the bill provided the administration with sufficient authority so that if the salmon runs were not fully protected, the responsibility would rest squarely on the Secretary of Commerce.[123]

Representative John Rankin of Mississippi said that in traveling along the coast of British Columbia he saw a large number of people out in small fishing boats making their living from the sea, but that in Alaska he found the traps had virtually driven the little man from the fishery. He concluded that if Congress wanted to encourage people to move to the territory and make it their permanent home, the trap should be done away with altogether.[124] Representative Davis responded that while a great many members of Congress agreed, including himself, the committee had worked hard to prepare a bill to which there could be no serious objection. He feared that if too many prohibitions were included, the bill would "be smothered and go the way that former bills have."[125] Representative Rankin complained that, in his experience on the committee, whenever the canners wanted something from Congress the people of Alaska were not able to pay the expenses to come to Washington to testify, and so the committee invariably heard only one side of the

[122] *Ibid.*, p. 2.
[123] U.S. *Congressional Record*, 68th Cong., 1st Sess., p. 5451.
[124] *Ibid.*, p. 5451.
[125] *Ibid.*, p. 5452.

question. Representative Davis agreed and was applauded from the floor when he said that the rights of the citizens and natives of Alaska should be made paramount over the interests of the packers who as a rule were nonresidents interested only in exploiting the fishery.[126]

The bill was debated again on April 9, and Delegate Sutherland offered an amendment making it unlawful to place traps in bays, inlets, or estuaries less than three miles wide or within one mile of the mouth of any stream.[127] The impact of the amendment would be to eliminate the vast majority of traps. The delegate noted that this proposal had been rejected earlier by the committee primarily because of strong pressures brought to bear by the "predatory interests" in California, a state that for forty years had itself barred the use of traps in catching salmon.[128] The congressmen from both California and Washington strongly objected to the proposed amendment. Representative Free of California claimed that if the amendment were adopted "you will put the fishery into the hands of a few Indians in Alaska,"[129] and Representative Miller of Washington said the decision should be left to the Secretary, who would have the power under the proposed bill to prohibit traps if he chose. Delegate Sutherland responded that this was true, "but judging from past experience they never will."[130]

In an attempt to counteract the Sutherland amendment, Representative Hadley of Washington argued that purse seines were more destructive than fishing by traps, and an amendment to the Sutherland amendment was introduced to similarly limit purse seines.[131]

Representative Rankin concluded the debate with a rousing speech. He pointed out that Congress had just appropriated $57 million to build a railroad in Alaska for the specific purpose of stimulating development and settlement, and that many more millions of dollars had been spent to accommodate the new settlers. "If you are going to encourage people to go there and live and make their home there," he asked, "why do you not protect them and give them some way in which to make a living?" He concluded

[126] *Ibid.*, p. 5452.
[127] *Ibid.*, p. 5956.
[128] *Ibid.*, p. 5976.
[129] *Ibid.*, p. 5977.
[130] *Ibid.*, p. 5979.
[131] *Ibid.*, pp. 5973, 5978.

that he would support the amendments "in order that we may save Alaska for Alaskans and give their children and their children's children some method by which they can earn an honest living."[132]

The amendments were brought to a vote and, to the surprise of nearly everyone, both were agreed to by the House.[133] Representative Hadley then offered another amendment to exempt the rich red salmon runs of Bristol Bay from the weekly closed period provided in the bill. He claimed that the Department of Commerce had been able to obtain an adequate escapement in the region in the past and that there was no need for such a closed period in the area. This was an exemption the salmon packers strongly favored, and the amendment was rejected. A quorum was called by Representative Rankin and the bill as previously amended was voted upon by the House and passed.[134]

In the Senate the bill was referred to the Committee on Commerce chaired by Senator Wesley Jones of Washington. Senator Jones submitted the bill to Secretary of Commerce Hoover for comment. Hoover reported that the department had been laboring under obsolete laws and limited authority for many years and that there was an urgent need for the legislation. As to the House amendments, the Secretary believed there would be many difficulties in the administration of the provision. He noted that the amendments would have very serious effects upon the industry since the total pack would be reduced by about 37 per cent, or nearly 2 million cases. He concluded that curtailment of operations to conserve fish was justified but that "any unnecessary prohibition of the taking of fish spells unnecessary destruction of investment. . . ."[135]

In the latter part of April the bill was reported out of committee with an amendment striking out the House amendments. In the Senate report accompanying the bill, the committee said it did not presume to pass on the merits of the House amendments but rather was satisfied that if the provisions were not struck out there would be no legislation passed at all during the session.[136] Later, concern

---

[132] *Ibid.*, p. 5979.

[133] *Ibid.*, p. 5979. (Sutherland amendment, ayes 74, naes 63; amendment to the amendment, ayes 46, naes 31.)

[134] *Ibid.*, p. 5980.

[135] U.S. Congress, Senate, Committee on Commerce, *Protection of the Fisheries of Alaska, Report to Accompany H.R. 8143,* Senate Report No. 449, 68th Cong., 1st Sess., April 21, 1924, pp. 3-4.

[136] *Ibid.*, p. 2.

began to develop that the bill would not be called for consideration in the Senate before adjournment of the session. Senator King of Utah introduced a resolution demanding that all department orders and regulations granting exclusive fishing rights to corporations in Alaska under the reservation policy be immediately rescinded, and he noted on the floor of the Senate that he was prompted to offer the resolution in an effort to force some action on the part of Senator Jones who he feared had buried the bill.[137] Senator Jones agreed that the bill would be called up for consideration as soon as possible, and on May 26 the bill was finally taken up on the floor of the Senate.

The Senate voted in favor of striking the House amendments. Senator Jones then offered an amendment to lessen the discretion of the Secretary with regard to weekly closed periods, a change the packers had been pushing. To counterbalance this, he offered a second amendment at the request of the delegate from Alaska adding a clause that nothing in the Act would curtail the powers already granted the territorial legislature. The delegate wanted to make sure that the new legislation would in no way alter or nullify the territory's power to tax the fisheries which for many years the packers had been fighting in the federal courts. Both amendments were agreed to by the Senate.[138] Just before the vote on the bill a letter from President Coolidge was read urging that the bill be passed promptly as the fishing season for the year was rapidly approaching. Said the President:

> I am advised that this bill in its present form affords ample power for the preservation of this great but fast failing source of food supply for the American people.
>
> It necessarily means curtailment of fishing operations. No conservation measure can be worthy of the name unless it reduces the amount of fish that may be taken. . . . Reduction necessarily means sacrifice for those now engaged in these fisheries, but selfish considerations must always yield to the public interest. In the long run it is in the interest of both canners and fishermen. . . .[139]

The Senate passed the bill as amended.

The House disagreed with the Senate amendments and asked for a conference, but in the conference committee the House receded

---

[137] U.S. *Congressional Record,* 68th., 1st Sess., p. 7160.
[138] *Ibid.*, pp. 9519-9520.
[139] *Ibid.*, p. 9703.

and agreed to all of the Senate amendments including the Senate action which struck the House amendments.[140] The bill, as finally amended, passed both houses and was signed by President Coolidge on June 6, 1924.[141]

Between 1906 and 1924 a total of forty-two different bills had been introduced in Congress dealing with some aspect of the "protection and regulation of the Alaska fisheries" and full congressional hearings had been held on a dozen different occasions.[142] With passage of the White Act a compromise among the interests was finally effected which resulted in the extension of the government's authority to regulate the fishery, and the establishment of a definite policy toward the Alaska salmon fishery, a policy which was to prevail throughout the remainder of the period of federal control. The compromise, it should be noted, came at a time when the industry was facing a serious economic crisis.

Under the Act broad powers were lodged in the Secretary of Commerce to create fishing areas in any of the waters of the territory over which the United States had jurisdiction, and within such areas he could fix the size and character of fishing gear, limit or prohibit fishing, make regulations as to the time, means, method and extent of fishing within each of the various areas as he deemed advisable. However, every regulation had to be of general applicability within the particular area to which it applied, and it was provided emphatically that

> no exclusive or several right of fishery shall be granted therein, nor shall any citizen of the United States be denied the right to take, prepare, cure, or preserve fish or shellfish in any area of the waters of Alaska where fishing is permitted by the Secretary of Commerce.[143]

Under this provision the Secretary was denied the power to control and regulate the amount of gear in the fishery. The reservation concept, which had been a means to this end, was automatically nullified, and on the day following passage of the Act, the Executive Orders creating the two existing reserves were revoked by the President.[144]

---

[140] *Ibid.*, pp. 9869, 9890, 10297, 10298, 10551.

[141] U.S. Congress, *An Act For the Protection of the Fisheries of Alaska . . .*, Public Law 204, 68th Cong., 1st Sess., 1924. (43 Stat. 464).

[142] Revealed in the indexes to the *Congressional Record* during the period.

[143] Public Law 204, *op. cit.*, Section 1.

[144] U.S. Department of Commerce, *Annual Report of the Secretary of Commerce, 1924* (Washington: U.S. Government Printing office, 1925), p. 156.

A unique provision in the new bill was the declaration of congressional intent that not less than 50 per cent of the salmon should be allowed to escape to the spawning beds to perpetuate the supply, and in any year in which the runs of salmon in any waters showed signs of diminishing "there shall be a correspondingly increased escapement of fish therefrom."[145] This congressional policy was not based on definite scientific knowledge as to the percentage of escapement needed to perpetuate the runs, for no such information was available, and in later years the efficacy of the general rule-of-thumb formula was seriously questioned by the scientists as they began to learn more about the life-cycle and habits of the salmon. Nevertheless, it was clear that Congress expected the federal agency to measure both catches and escapements accurately, and to adjust regulations to allow an ample escapement to the spawning grounds.

Another significant and altogether new extension of authority was the provision giving bureau employees the legal power to arrest violators and to seize gear operating illegally. Fines up to $5,000 and 90 days in prison could be invoked for violation of the law. All boats and equipment found in violation were to be forfeited to the United States and sold at public auction.

The White Act was widely hailed as a major landmark in conservation philosophy and technique that would ensure the healthy perpetuation of the Alaska salmon resource. An editorial in the industry trade journal stated that passage of the Alaska Fisheries Act

> means the final establishment of a definite policy by the federal government for the protection of this great resource and provides means whereby the salmon runs of the territory may be maintained permanently as the basis of a productive industry and a source of profit to the community. . . . The monopolistic features of the fishery reservations, with the principle of exclusive franchises, are ended.[146]

Secretary Hoover called passage of the Act one of the most significant steps ever accomplished in the preservation of a sea fishery, and he warned that the industry should be prepared for the reductions in operations that would be required for the purpose of conservation.[147] New and more restrictive regulations were immediately issued and the Alaska activities of the Bureau of Fisheries were con-

[145] Public Law 204, *op. cit.*, Section 2.
[146] *Pacific Fisherman*, June 1924, p. 16.
[147] *Ibid.*, p. 5.

siderably increased.[148] As early as September, 1924, in a speech delivered before the sixth annual convention of the U.S. Fisheries Association at Atlantic City, Secretary Hoover claimed that under the Act the department had "vigorously stopped destruction and started rejuvenation of these fisheries."[149]

But these words represented wishful thinking, for certain forces were already operating to make a mockery of the increased efforts of the bureau to curtail production for purposes of conservation. In the first place, the economic forces that had depressed the markets for salmon during the postwar years largely disappeared in the spring of 1924. In the second place, passage of the White Act and the immediate announcement of new and drastic regulations led to gloomy forebodings as to output. It was conservatively estimated by some, for instance, that these new fishing restrictions were certain to reduce the Alaska pack by at least 25 per cent.[150] This, in conjunction with the prospects for expanded markets, induced a sharp rise in salmon prices and a renewed interest on the part of packers and brokers. In effect, the market outlook was such that increased restrictions served to induce increased preparations by the salmon packers. As a result, the 1924 seasonal pack turned out to be the largest ever produced in the territory with the exception of the two peak war years.

At the end of the year it was reported in the industry trade journal that the season had been "a most profitable one for the great majority of packers, . . . placing all in a position for an aggressive campaign next year."[151] One of the basic reasons given for the optimistic outlook was the likelihood of even more stringent government restrictions which were sure to induce still higher prices. Said one of the large salmon brokers:

> A clarion note could be sounded to which salmon packers should tune their ears. Here it is: in 1925 it will be events outside and not within the industry that will make the price trend . . . and it will

[148] For example, while in 1923 the Bureau operated 8 vessels and employed 50 men in Alaska, in the 1924 season there were 10 vessels and a total of 146 men involved in guarding the resource. (See: *Alaska Fisheries and Fur-Seal Industries in 1924, op. cit.* pp. 91-92.)

[149] *Annual Report of the Secretary of Commerce, 1924, op. cit.*, p. 25.

[150] *Pacific Fisherman,* January 1925 (Yearbook), p. 81.

[151] *Ibid.,* October 1924, p. 14.

sweep all the salmon you can pack into consumption. The character of the business has changed, and the days of 1920 are no more.[152]

Regardless of these ominous forewarnings, the White Act continued to be acclaimed as the savior of the Alaska salmon resource.

---

[152] *Ibid.*, January 1925 (Yearbook), p. 84.

6 *Conservation under the White Act*

In spite of statements made earlier by President Coolidge, Secretary of Commerce Hoover, and other high government officials that conservation of the resource would require a reduction in output, for well over a decade following passage of the White Act the trend in the total pack continued its general upward sweep. Surprisingly, this trend seemed not to alarm either the industry or the government. In fact, it was frequently cited as evidence of the healthy condition of the resource stemming from the success of the regulatory program.

In 1928 the Commissioner of Fisheries delivered a paper before the American Fisheries Society entitled "Alaska Salmon—An Achievement in Conservation." He stated that the future of the fishery was most promising and there was no reason whatever to prevent the industry from increasing to greater and greater proportions until the maximum productivity of the waters was reached.[1] In that same year the editor of the industry trade journal called attention to the increasing production and cited this as a triumph of conservation that would have been impossible had protective action not been taken. He concluded that while unfavorable natural conditions might occasionally cause a poor run, there was no longer any

---

[1] *Pacific Fisherman,* September 28, 1928, p. 13.

danger of general depletion so long as the present policies were carried out.[2]

In the eyes of the industry the person primarily responsible for these ideal conditions was Secretary of Commerce Herbert Hoover. His work in saving the salmon resource was praised as an outstanding example of "practical idealism made effective," and his regulatory program was described as "firmness without oppression." The trade journal exclaimed:

> Compare the quiet accomplishments of Herbert Hoover, for instance, with the clamorous but fruitless turmoil created by Gifford Pinchot and his followers who seized upon the conservation question as a national political issue. . . . Pinchotism made a vast amount of noise for a time, but . . . it never accomplished anything of value. . . . He [Secretary Hoover] has set a precedence, not of talk and theory, but of action and results—a precedence which the country has greatly needed not in the fisheries alone, but in many resources such as timber, minerals, petroleum and waterpower.[3]

These were great words and stirring thoughts, but they bore no relation to the real situation and in no way revealed the true condition of the fishery. What was happening amounted to a repetition on a much larger scale of what had taken place two decades earlier following passage of the 1906 Act. The compromise among the interests which resulted in passage of the White Act came at a time when the market for canned salmon was in a demoralized state and there was a concomitant need to curtail production for practical business reasons. Under these conditions "conservation" had a strong economic appeal for the packers. But at the time the Act was being signed into law, the United States was entering a period of great industrial growth and prosperity which had an immensely favorable impact upon the salmon market. The number of operating canneries and units of gear in the fishery were rapidly expanded and heavy investments were made in modernizing and otherwise improving the efficiency of both canneries and fishing apparatus. The larger companies attempted to strengthen their competitive position through large-scale purchases of smaller independent concerns, and another run of consolidations and mergers of operations occurred as companies sought to cut costs, raise output, and increase profits.

---

[2] *Ibid.*, p. 24.
[3] *Ibid.*, October 1928, p. 15.

The industry's reaction to these favorable economic conditions was exemplified in a statement made by the president of the Pacific American Fisheries Company in 1928. The company had recently absorbed the salmon-canning properties of the great Wilson Fisheries Company, and through this transaction had become the largest producer of canned salmon, accounting for about 12 per cent of the entire American pack. The president, E. B. Deming, outlined his optimistic views for the future of the industry and stated that a policy of further expansion would be followed vigorously by his company. On the important question of the future outlook for the supply, he concluded blithely that the bureau had everything well under control in Alaska and that knowledge of the habits of the salmon coupled with government regulation had made it possible to regulate the escapement to assure the supply.[4]

Other important mergers took place, including one of the largest transactions in the history of the Pacific salmon fishery when, in 1928, the Skinner and Eddy Corporation purchased the properties of the Alaska Consolidated Canneries, Inc. This brought the greater part of the output of pink salmon under one ownership.[5] The salmon brokerage business and other related segments of the industry were also strongly involved in the merger movement.

The various associations of canners and brokers found the time opportune to enlarge their programs and strengthen their positions in the industry. The Association of Pacific Fisheries, the primary lobbying organization for the larger packers, embarked upon a large-scale national advertising program with the aim of enlarging consumer demand and increasing the price of the product. It sought higher tariffs on canned salmon to protect the home markets from threats of Oriental salmon. A group of independent packing concerns (i.e., primarily the smaller canning concerns that did not have their own sales departments) formed a new organization known as the Northwest Salmon Canners Association which quickly became a potent force in the industry. Aside from lobbying activities, one of the basic purposes of the new organization was "to correct cer-

[4] *Ibid.*, p. 15. (The impact of Deming's economic views were great, for he was also a partner in the Deming and Gould brokerage concern which marketed a large part of the total salmon pack, and he was director of a financial organization which owned six banks in Seattle with a capitalization of around $35 million that financed many of the packers' activities in Alaska.)

[5] *Ibid.*, January 1929 (Yearbook), p. 56, and *Ibid.*, January 1929, p. 7.

tain market abuses," and the practice was established of holding joint meetings with the Pacific Canned Salmon Brokers Association. While it was constantly maintained that the associations were two entirely separate and distinct organizations, they both chose to elect the same person to act as executive officer. This move served greatly to increase the solidarity among important factors within the industry.[6]

Under such dynamic business conditions the connotation that conservation would require a reduction in total output was quietly forgotten by the industry, and in its place an opposite criterion was substituted: that the government conservation program was successful as long as total output continued to increase year after year. Given the economic conditions that prevailed, this shift in the industry's viewpoint is not difficult to comprehend. What is difficult to understand is how the Bureau of Fisheries was deluded by the same thinking.

For one thing, a feeling of complacency was generated at the top policy level in Washington, D. C. by the continual praise and assurances received from the industry. Furthermore, the packers, through their various organizations and associations, had attained such a strong position in the policy making process that important decisions by bureau officials concerning the regulation of the salmon fishery seldom were freely made. For example, shortly after passage of the White Act the Commissioner of Fisheries announced a series of regulations designed to reduce output, but as pressure from the industry mounted the restrictions were progressively liberalized "to avoid any immediate marked disturbance of an established fishery."[7] In the following year the Commissioner admitted that the earlier regulations had been conservative in character and he warned that more drastic regulations would be promulgated if fishing intensity continued to increase. When further restrictions were applied, however, they were calculated not to curtail production but, in the bureau's own words, to maintain the status quo. Even in this lesser aim they failed miserably. Total production continued to increase as fishing and canning intensity mounted. The bureau seemed wholly unable to make an independent decision and carry it through.

---

[6] *Ibid.*, April 1930, p. 14.
[7] *Ibid.*, September 1928, p. 13.

Another factor was the lack of accurate scientific knowledge about the resource upon which a vigorous regulatory program could be justified and defended. In 1925 an International Pacific Salmon conference was held in which fishery officials from the governments of Washington, Oregon, California, and British Columbia, as well as from the United States and Canada, met for the first time to discuss the status of scientific research on the salmon. It was brought out in the proceedings that although scientific study had been going on for nearly a half century, the actual knowledge of the movements and habits of the salmon was lamentably small, and the widest divergence of opinion still existed on a great many questions of vital concern in properly regulating the fishery. It was remarked by one scientist that "if we tried to conduct agriculture on the basis of such ignorance, anyone would think we were daft."[8]

An accomplishment of the conference was the establishment of an informal organization known as the International Pacific Salmon Investigation Federation to develop and carry out a cooperative research program along the coast. Grandiose plans were laid for a unified program of research centering on some of the basic questions. But with rising prices, packs, and profits, it was difficult to generate any real concern within the industry or the general public, and without such backing appropriation of the necessary funds was impossible. Consequently only a few of the many proposed studies were actually completed. When an occasional investigation revealed that all was not as rosy as it seemed—as in the case of a study by bureau biologists in 1928 which revealed strong evidence of depletion of the great red salmon runs in Bristol Bay[9]—the findings were lost in a sea of optimism.

The bureau itself did much to perpetrate this optimism. Its annual escapement reports, which were given wide circulation, provide a good example. Each year the reports revealed the bureau's official view of the extent of salmon escapements into the Alaska streams measured by the 50 per cent requirement of the White Act, and each year the reports revealed that escapements were either

[8] *Ibid.*, April 1925, p. 3.

[9] Willis H. Rich and Edward Ball, *Statistical Review of the Alaska Salmon Fisheries*, Bureau of Fisheries Document No. 1041 (Washington: U.S. Government Printing Office, 1928), 54 pp. (It was concluded that if depletion continued at the present rate, within the next two or three decades the formerly magnificent runs would be commercially worthless.)

excellent or satisfactory, and only on rare occasion was it ever indicated that the escapement in a particular area might have been poor. Frequently the reports concluded with statements such as: "No alarm for the future is felt by the Bureau of Fisheries" or "More salmon reached the spawning grounds under better conditions than in any previous year."[10] How the bureau with its limited facilities and personnel in Alaska was able to measure these escapements in order to make such positive statements is a moot question, but probably the opinions of the packers in the various fishing regions were heavily relied upon.

That the packers were satisfied with the relaxed policies of the federal government was evinced by the full support given Herbert Hoover in his campaign for the presidency in the fall of 1928. The canned-salmon industry was eager to have him elected for two reasons, both of which were the subject of numerous editorials in the industry trade journal. First, it was said that his election would undoubtedly assure four and perhaps eight years of continuous fishery administration along the same lines. Second, some of the major packers were beginning to worry about possible antitrust violations, and the industry as a whole was in agreement with Hoover's general opposition to government interference in the regulation of business.[11] And indeed when Hoover was elected, the packers had every reason to be satisfied. The existing Commissioner of Fisheries was retained, with an avowed assurance that regulatory policies would be maintained in substantially the same form; the antitrust laws as construed and enforced by the new administration afforded business the widest possible latitude.[12]

In the early 1930's the salmon packers joined in an effort to get Congress to relax further the antitrust laws with respect to certain natural resources including the fisheries. The purpose was to permit operators in such industries to agree among themselves to balance production against consumer requirements "in the interest of conservation." It was pointed out in a statement pertaining to the salmon fisheries that while the federal government had been sanctioning trade organization activities "looking toward a more

---

[10] For example see: *Pacific Fisherman*, January 1928 (Yearbook), p. 100, and January 1931 (Yearbook), p. 107.

[11] *Ibid.*, July 1928, pp. 11-13, 24.

[12] Reported in: *Ibid.*, July 1929, p. 23.

orderly conduct of business through cooperative effort" there was no assurance that this administrative policy might not be radically altered in the future.[13] Tremendous support was generated in favor of the idea and President Hoover recommended that Congress give careful consideration to the proposal. The industry trade journal gave its full support and warned the packers to be more cautious in their efforts to control prices until the necessary legislation was passed.[14]

Although Congress did not act favorably on the proposal, the movement was highly revealing. It was obvious that this was an attempt to legalize certain monopolistic practices that had been going on within the industry for a number of years. Furthermore, the packers were in the anomalous position of attempting to justify greater monopolistic controls on the basis of conservation needs, while at the same time maintaining that the existing federal conservation program under the White Act was meeting these needs adequately. Either the packers did not actually believe their own public pronouncements regarding the success of federal programs in maintaining the resource or they were merely using the conservation argument for more mundane pecuniary motives.

As the country moved from these flourishing times into the depths of the depression, economic and political changes occurred which had a cataclysmic influence upon the fishery. Cost of production had risen greatly during the prosperous boom years. When the market price began to sag the packers were faced with a severe cost–price squeeze. Beginning in 1930 the packers attempted to revive the price by voluntary curtailment of production through temporary joint operations and consolidations, but with little success. When the Commissioner of Fisheries proposed regulations in that same year to materially reduce the number of traps, for the first time in the history of the industry the packers agreed to the plan. The packers reasoned that such a move might help to reduce costs of production by allowing them to close the less profitable traps temporarily without losing their control over the sites, and they thought it might also lead to a reduction in the size of the pink and chum packs, thus helping to increase the price.[15]

---

[13] *Ibid.*, May 1931, p. 29.
[14] *Ibid.*, p. 29.
[15] *Ibid.*, December 1930, pp. 9, 13.

As a result, both the number of traps and the number of operating canneries were reduced by around 50 per cent, but the reductions actually had very little impact on output. There had been such an overcapitalization in canneries and fishing gear during the prosperous years that the industry entered the depression with a tremendous excess production capacity. The remaining units were operated much more intensely and efficiently in an effort to cut production costs further, and the over-all result was a continued upward trend in the total pack in spite of the sagging prices.

As the depression deepened so did the intensity of the conflict between labor and capital and between residents and nonresidents. The salmon packers, who had enjoyed a high degree of economic and political autonomy for many years, now were forced into a painful struggle to maintain a semblance of the status quo. As the labor movement began to make strides throughout the country, the fishermen and cannery workers in the salmon industry organized and became affiliated with strong international unions. The canners were faced with demands for higher wages and better working conditions in the canneries, and higher fish prices to the fishermen. They were faced with the necessity of giving up the Oriental contract system whereby for decades Chinese and other cheap labor from the West coast had been ruthlessly exploited in the Alaska canneries. They were faced with bitter jurisdictional strikes among unions striving for power which annually delayed or completely tied up preparations for the seasonal packs. They were faced with a now unified resentment among residents of the territory who sought to have the fishery provide more of them with a better living.

In short, the canners were confronted with chaotic conditions that intensified the cost–price squeeze. Further, they were threatened with a considerable loss of influence in the political process as the new groups began to bring their recently won powers to bear upon the Bureau of Fisheries in a direction that was antagonistic to the packers' interests.

The packers immediately responded to these threats with a series of moves to further strengthen their internal organization. Late in 1933 the Association of Pacific Fisheries passed a resolution calling for closer collaboration with the Northwest Salmon Canners Association and the Pacific Canned Salmon Brokers Association to bring about a greater unity of purpose in dealing with the urgent problems.[16] A plan of joint deliberations was adopted and a number of joint committees were formed to handle labor problems, representation in Washington, D. C., territorial relations, and other matters of special importance.

Later, under the National Industrial Recovery Act, the packers were drawn into even closer formal relations through the creation of an organization known as the Canned Salmon Industry which drew up and administered the NRA code for them. The new organization held great powers in the setting of prices and production, in labor matters, and in other important spheres affecting the industry. It proved so valuable that when the Supreme Court declared the NRA legislation unconstitutional, the packers decided to continue the organization on a voluntary basis. For a time the executive office served as a central coordinator for the many joint committees of the various associations, but the organization was eventually incorporated as the Canned Salmon Industry, Inc., and it became the principal organizational unit for all factors in the industry, embracing more than 90 per cent of the entire production of canneries in Alaska.[17] This closely knit association was highly effective in all facets of its work and remained the most powerful industry organization throughout the remainder of the federal period.

The packers also increased their influence on the national level through closer ties with the potent National Fisheries Association with central offices in Washington, D. C., and through strong participation on the federal Fishery Advisory Committee, which provided a direct communications link with the Secretary of Commerce. For a number of years this committee was chaired by one of the leading Alaska salmon packers.

With the coming of the New Deal, the Bureau of Fisheries launched a bold approach to the conservation of the Alaska salmon fishery which reflected the thinking of the new administration as it attempted to lead the country out of the depression. Spokesman for the change was Frank T. Bell who replaced Henry O'Malley as Commissioner of Fisheries.

Shortly after taking office Commissioner Bell made an extended tour of the territory. He held hearings in every fishing district in

[16] *Ibid.*, December 1933, p. 9.
[17] *Ibid.*, January 1940, p. 9.

Alaska and conferred with the packers in Seattle. A month after his trip he issued a statement which amounted to a sweeping change in the bureau's policies and its relations with the interest groups.

Commissioner Bell made it clear that in his view the bureau's responsibility in Alaska was not merely to regulate the fisheries for the sole purpose of maintaining the resource. Economic and social implications of the regulations would also be considered. He said (1) the entire conservation program would be brought in line with the fundamental economic policies of the President's program, and especially with his policy of spreading employment; (2) there were far too many salmon traps in the Alaska fishery and while he had no intention of entirely eliminating this form of gear, his policy would be to reduce their number further and otherwise restrict their operations with the aim of strengthening the position of local and independent fishermen; and (3) the bureau would relax some of the restrictions on seiners and gillnetters and make other concessions to the desires of the Alaska residents as long as such actions did not conflict with the fundamental principles of conservation.

Bell insisted that the packers make all possible provision to use the catch of independent fishermen, and he warned that if they did not comply he would curtail trap operations until an ample outlet was assured for the independent gear throughout the season. On other matters, he declared that the cumbersome and inefficient enforcement and patrol system would be completely reorganized and that patrol boats would be largely replaced by seaplanes. On the hatchery question he took the view that the work of government hatcheries was a complete waste of public funds which actually constituted an unjustified subsidy to the industry, and he ordered the immediate closure of the two remaining government hatcheries in Alaska. Finally, he concluded that a vigorous program would be maintained to assure the permanence of the resource but that "the human element" would receive every possible consideration.[18]

Commissioner Bell ran into extreme difficulties in attempting to carry out his program. As the depression heightened, federal funds became scarce, and the bureau was handicapped by marked decreases in the already inadequate funds for its Alaska operations. Enforcement, patrol, and other essential management activities

---

[18] Reported in: *Pacific Fisherman,* July 1933, p. 21; August 1933, p. 12.

had to be reduced accordingly, and the meager scientific research work then in progress was curtailed. The bureau pointed out to the Budget Bureau and the House Appropriations Committee that scientific research was valueless unless undertaken continuously over a period of years and that any interruption through lack of appropriations meant that the significance of the previous work would be lost. It was pointed out that the federal government's obligation to the fisheries was far greater in Alaska than elsewhere and that the biological problems of the territorial salmon fisheries were entitled to much greater consideration than those of any other district.

But the appropriations continued to lag and by 1935 the amount allotted for biological investigations in Alaska had sunk to $16,530. The Bureau of Fisheries sent a plea to the canned-salmon industry pointing out that at least $115,000 was urgently needed for this work during the year. It was pointed out explicitly that unless members of the industry brought the matter forcefully to the attention of their congressmen, it was unlikely that any further funds would be made available for the proper conduct of these vital studies.[19] When the appropriation came up before the committee, however, no members of Congress appeared to plead the bureau's case and the appropriations for management and scientific investigation of the Alaska salmon fishery continued at a dangerously low level.

Commissioner Bell also ran into exceptionally acute and incisive political pressures. His efforts to "humanize" the program ushered in an era of vicious conflict as each of the major groups attempted to maximize its benefits from the annual harvests at the expense of others. The clamor over the annual regulations became automatic and unyielding. The Commissioner had no difficulty liberalizing the regulations according to his announced program so that operators of smaller types of gear had a better opportunity to ply their vocation. As a result the number of seine boats actually increased considerably during this period. But when he attempted to follow through with correlative restrictive measures which were absolutely necessary for the success of his program, he ran into heavy resistance. A great outcry arose from those who were ad-

[19] *Ibid.*, April 1936, p. 20.

versely influenced. There were charges of corrupt administration, unethical practices, favoritism, and collusion.

Under pressure the Commissioner relented, first in one place and then another, and in 1934 and 1935 general market conditions began improving and the total number of traps increased. Except for a brief respite, the intensity of fishing effort continued upward as did the total pack of canned salmon, and by the mid-1930s the bold new program that Commissioner Bell had launched so forcefully was all but forgotten.

Bell realized what was happening but was unable to do anything about it. This was indicated in a statement in 1935 when he said that "unfortunately our political system of government permits well-organized minorities to secure the enactment of regulations that frequently benefit the few at the expense of the many."[20] As Ernest Gruening mentioned in his discussion of this era, going over the head of the Fisheries Commissioner to the cabinet officers and invoking the friendly offices of one's senators was established practice when the Commissioner would not yield to pressure. For example, at congressional hearings in the late 1930s, one of the more forceful and outspoken salmon packers said bluntly: "I went to Secretary Roper and saw him right in his office. In 1936 I told him to take his regulation book and throw it into the Potomac River."[21]

The controversy over the ownership and use of traps rose to a white heat during the depression. The large reduction in stationary gear that occurred in the early 1930s had the effect of greatly increasing the average catch of the remaining units, and the value of each operating trap was increased accordingly. Control of a single select site could easily provide the owner with an annual net income of $30,000 even during depression times, and a good trap site could be sold for many times that figure. To the packers, who held or controlled most of the sites, the traps represented not only a highly valuable economic asset but they were considered absolutely necessary as a means of maintaining control over fish prices in the face of the rising power of the fishermen's unions. To both

[20] *Ibid.*, April 1935, p. 20.

[21] Reported in: Ernest Gruening, *The State of Alaska* (New York: Random House, 1954), pp. 400-401. (In reference to the statement of Nick Bez in *Hearings . . . on H.R. 162,* 1939, pp. 145-146.)

resident and nonresident fishermen, the existence of company-controlled traps represented a major obstacle to their progress.

At the height of the conflict in the mid-1930s the Alaska congressional delegate, Anthony J. Dimond, introduced a bill in the House to prohibit the use of traps in all the waters of Alaska. The congressional hearing held by the Merchant Marine and Fisheries Committee on the proposed legislation early in 1936 provides valuable insight into the attitudes of the various interest groups and the governing agency at this critical point in the history of the exploitation of the resource.[22] It will be recalled that 1936 was the year in which the total pack of canned salmon reached an all-time high of over eight million cases and then began its sharp and continuous decline.

While the salmon packers had been unable to organize even a modicum of support behind the bureau's appropriations requests before Congress, when it came to a matter that directly threatened their pocketbook, such as this bill to eliminate traps, they had no difficulty in forging a massive well-planned campaign to defeat the measure. Months before the hearings, the industry selected a committee, composed of the presidents of three of the largest packing concerns, to design the strategy and make the necessary preparations. Weeks were spent in Washington, D. C., lining up support. A letter was sent out across the nation to officials of other fishery associations; to wholesalers, retailers, and other customers of canned salmon; and to businessmen, lawyers, and other influential persons asking for their active support in defeating the measure. Special emphasis was given to the states of Massachusetts and Virginia where the chairmen of the House and Senate fisheries committees resided.

The letter contained a forceful expression of the canners' position:

> The salmon fishery of Alaska has been built up to the healthiest condition that it has ever been, with every prospect of this condition continuing. Traps assist in conservation because they are so much more easily regulated than gear which is on a small boat and can be moved around at will. . . . It is certainly the height of folly when a natural

[22] U.S. Congress, House, Merchant Marine and Fisheries Committee, *Fish Traps in Alaska, Hearings . . . on H.R. 4254 and H.R. 8213,* 74th Cong., 2nd Sess., 1936, 288 pp.

resource is in such sound condition and the industry based upon it is paying good wages and conducting its business in a satisfactory manner, to allow one selfish element to wreck the whole structure.[23]

A list containing the names of the members of the House committee was enclosed with the letter, and it was requested that the respondents do everything possible through the chairman or any member of the committee with whom they were acquainted to have this bill unfavorably reported so that it would not get beyond the committee hearings.[24] As a result, before the hearings were opened each committee member had received from all over the country a barrage of letters opposing the bill. The canners feared Congress might be in a mood to act should a bill to eliminate traps get to the floor.

At the hearings Edward W. Allen, a prominent Seattle attorney, was given the job of directing the canners' testimony against the bill. One of the key witnesses was J. M. Gilbert who represented the Alaska-Pacific Salmon Company. He opposed the bill on the grounds that it was confiscatory, that it defeated the ends of conservation, and that it prejudiced the interests of the consumer. He asserted that if traps were eliminated the other forms of gear would not be able to catch enough fish to keep the industry supplied at the level required for economic operations. On the question of the effect of traps upon the aboriginal population, Gilbert painted a glowing but untrue picture of the condition of the Alaska Indians. He said the wives were dressing in high heels and good clothes, that they lived in fair homes and educated their children, and that anybody representing them as being in a miserable condition was not speaking truly. He lauded the Bureau of Fisheries for its effective control under the White Act. He emphasized that "conservation had been accomplished" and that the industry was now getting larger production without any harm to the streams or to the future runs. When asked about the possible need for further restrictive measures to protect the resource, Gilbert concluded:

I think instead of decreasing catch, it will be possible to increase it as the runs build up. I think the Bureau of Fisheries can and may possibly say for the benefit of this hearing that commercial fishing has

[23] *Ibid.*, pp. 282-288.
[24] *Ibid.*, p. 287.

tended to increase the runs by reason of the fact that overescapement in certain streams will almost annihilate the runs. . . .

In other words, overescapement has been proven to be much worse than overcatch of fish, and the Bureau of Fisheries can support that statement I am sure.[25]

The testimony of A. W. Brindle, president of the Ward Cove Canning Company amplified Gilbert's. He asserted that if traps were abolished the seines would not be able to take enough fish, with the result that "too many fish would go up the streams and creeks; they would overcrowd and pollute the streams and in succeeding cycles the runs would be a failure."[26] He claimed that the pressure to abolish traps was the work of "professional agitators and radicals" active since as early as 1910. He said the runs had continually built up over the years as trap fishing expanded, "thus belying the assertions of these radicals about depletion."[27] He concluded emphatically that increasing annual packs proved there was no depletion of the salmon runs in the territory.

Others whom Allen brought forth to testify for the industry included the manager of the Massachusetts Fisheries Association and the Executive Secretary of the Middle Atlantic Fisheries Association in Virginia, both of whom spoke in general terms of the adverse effect the legislation would have upon the markets; a bank president from Alaska who contended that the measure would decrease territorial revenues; a small independent trap operator who spoke about how hard he had worked and sacrificed over the years to make a living from his traps, which would be completely wiped out by the legislation; a British Columbia packer who compared cannery operations and labor conditions in B.C. where traps had been outlawed with similar conditions in Alaska, and concluded that owing to traps the territory was much better off than B.C.; a lumberman who asserted that 65 per cent of the men in the woods of southeast Alaska were logging piles for traps and would be seriously influenced by elimination of traps. (This last witness reasoned further that the bill would result in a drop of federal receipts to the territory from the sale of forest products, cause a reduction in off-season employment, and result in a heavy

[25] *Ibid.*, pp. 110-150.
[26] *Ibid.*, p. 192.
[27] *Ibid.*, pp. 193-195.

drain on game because this source of food supply would become seriously depleted under heavy hunting by the unemployed workers.) Among those who filed briefs in opposition to the bill were a manufacturer of wire for traps, a number of small independent canners and trap owners, and a few businessmen and lawyers in Alaska.[28]

Delegate Anthony J. Dimond presented the main testimony in favor of the bill. The principal purpose, he said, was to help build up the population of Alaska and to help keep a fair part of the very enormous wealth in the territory where it was created.[29] He congratulated the opposition for their strategy in putting before the committee as their key witnesses two of the few remaining small cannery operators and one of the very few independent trap owners in Alaska. Said the delegate:

> The room is all but filled with the operators who pack on a big scale, but they have very carefully refrained from making any statement to the committee. It is indeed wise on their part to try to bring before the committee the plight of the comparatively small packer and of the independent trap owner if traps are to be abolished. But in this connection it is well to remember that the small packers have little stake in this measure as compared with the great corporations who practically dominate the salmon packing industry in Alaska.[30]

He noted there were few fishermen represented from Alaska on hand at the hearings, and that the few who had come made a considerable sacrifice to raise money for their expenses on the trip. As a result of their journey to Washington, said the delegate, some of these poor people will do without things that are really necessary for them this winter. "You can well realize that only an intolerable situation would lead these people to take of their extremely scanty earnings in order to raise sufficient funds to send representatives to Washington to give evidence in support of this bill."[31]

The delegate struck hard at the use of efficiency as the sole criteria in evaluating the use of traps. He pointed out that if this were the only goal then all fishing should be prohibited except

---

[28] *Ibid.*, pp. 150-212, 282-288.
[29] *Ibid.*, pp. 14, 28.
[30] *Ibid.*, p. 244.
[31] *Ibid.*, p. 27.

at the mouths of the rivers and streams by a few select weirs. While this would provide an extremely cheap product, he noted it would also add hundreds of productive fishermen to the relief roles. He asserted there was no element of confiscation in the bill because the trap owners had no prescriptive or permanent rights by law to the use of their trap sites. He asked that the members of the committee consider not only the relatively few trap operators who might be hurt by the passage of the bill, but also the thousands of residents of Alaska needing a better opportunity for obtaining the means of subsistence by their labors who would benefit by passage of the legislation.[32] As to the growing problem of enforcing regulations, the delegate called attention to the adverse impact the existence of traps had upon the fishermen's outlook toward conservation regulations:

> The permanent residents of Alaska, native as well as white, are anxious to comply with the law. . . . However . . . you cannot expect the fishermen to stand by and see millions of salmon caught in traps within sight of their humble homes whilst they and their families are deprived of the necessities of life. They are going to take the gift a kind nature offers so bountifully and feed their dear ones, *regulations or no regulations*.[33]

The delegate concluded that under the existing law the Commissioner had the power to open and close traps as he saw fit. Under such a law, he said, people assumed, however unjustly, that those who had traps, and particularly the best locations, held them through some kind of official favoritism. The situation was not conducive to respect of the bureau and the regulations it promulgated to control fishing.[34]

A fisherman from southeast Alaska asked why the federal government spends vast sums of money each year trying to populate Alaska, while on the other hand the same government "allows this special privilege and monopoly—the fishing trap—to rob and destroy natural resources of the country which, if continued, is bound to result in loss of population to the Territory."[35] Brief statements following a similar vein were presented by a half

[32] *Ibid.*, pp. 245-246.
[33] *Ibid.*, p. 87. (Italics added.)
[34] *Ibid.*, p. 29.
[35] *Ibid.*, pp. 40-41.

dozen other residents of the territory as well as by labor representatives from the West coast. Delegate Dimond introduced a series of petitions signed by hundreds of residents, and a number of sworn affidavits from local unions, fishermen's associations, native organizations, and various individuals, all asking for passage of the bill. Finally, he introduced a copy of a joint memorial from the Territorial Legislature to Congress asking for elimination of traps from Alaskan waters. The memorial had passed in 1935 by a vote of 24 to 1.

The impact of all this was lessened considerably when the packers introduced into the record various resolutions from the Chambers of Commerce in Juneau, Ketchikan, and Anchorage opposing passage of the legislation. This represented fruits reaped from the extensive public-relations campaign the canned-salmon industry had undertaken in the territory in recent years. Through selective local purchases of supplies and insurance, legal retainers, liberal placement of newspaper advertising, and other similar means, the industry had considerably increased its local support among certain business people in the coastal communities of Alaska.

No one from the Bureau of Fisheries appeared at the hearings to testify on the bill. However, the House committee sent the bill to the Department of Commerce for its views, and the department recommended an unfavorable report. It was asserted by the department that prohibition of traps was unnecessary either for reasons of conservation or upon economic grounds. It was noted that there was such a thing as having too many traps and the maximum of 799 in 1927 was too large, but that the 425 traps for the 1936 season provided a "happy medium." It was mentioned that the quality of trap-caught fish was of the very best and that it was easier to enforce conservation regulations with traps than with the other forms of gear. It was declared that the salmon fishery of Alaska was in fine shape as proved by the larger packs each year as well as by the reports from all regions showing excellent spawning escapements. "This," it was said, "may be taken as an indication of the success of the department's efforts in protecting and conserving the fisheries, including the regulation of fish traps."[36] The report amounted to little more than a summary of the packers'

[36] *Ibid.*, pp. 2-4.

viewpoint. As the packers hoped, the bill never got out of committee.

Conflict over the trap continued to mount and so did the bureau's self-satisfaction with its conservation program in Alaska. When the bureau's Alaska agent spoke to the salmon packers prior to the 1936 season, he referred to his agency's "cumulative success" in conserving and building up the northern salmon resource. He cautioned the packers not to count on short production to stiffen the market, and declared: "We look for lots of fish in Alaska and you fellows had better get ready to prepare them."[37] The packers did just that and, as will be recalled, the largest catch in the history of the fishery was produced that year. In his annual report for 1938, the Secretary of Commerce reviewed activities of the bureau during the previous year in Alaska and concluded that "the excellent condition of the fisheries in 1937 reflects the wisdom of conservation policies which have been in effect since 1924."[38]

In 1939 two biologists of the Bureau of Fisheries reported their findings on a study of southeast Alaska.[39] It was noted in the report that while there were fewer canneries than in the past, those in operation were exceedingly efficient owing to the introduction of high-speed equipment and other improvements, and that the potential productive capacity had actually increased in spite of the smaller number of canneries. A similar situation existed with regard to the intensity of the trap fishery, for "although the number of traps operated at the present time is comparatively low, their locations have been changed so that very few, if any, are operating at a disadvantage."[40] With respect to the purse seines, it was noted that intensity had been decidedly increased through increased efficiency of operations, introduction of diesel power, and the great increase in the total number of boats operated. The conclusion was that the intensity of the fishery and the capacity of the canneries was much greater than in any other period in the history of the industry. The question was then posed as to why the catch was holding, and the answer given was "the tightening up of fishery regulations since 1924" under conservation policies made possible

[37] *Pacific Fisherman,* January 1936, p. 11.

[38] U.S. Department of Commerce, *Annual Report of the Secretary of Commerce,* 1938 (Washington: U.S. Government Printing Office, 1939), p. 103.

[39] F. A. Davidson and A. E. Vaughn, "Cyclic Changes in Time of Southeast Alaska Pink Salmon Runs," *Pacific Fisherman,* February 1939, pp. 22-24.

[40] *Ibid.,* p. 22.

by the White Act.[41] The biologists did note that the intensity of the fishery had probably reached its maximum and that any increase was apt to be harmful, but even here complacency was evident.

Many were deceived by this self-aggrandizement by bureau and department officials. Governor of Alaska John W. Troy wrote in his annual report in 1936 that the federal efforts to preserve the salmon supply in Alaska had been agreeably successful and that it would be a long time, if ever, before there would be any alarm or fear that the salmon might become exhausted.[42] After a thorough study of the policies and programs of federal agencies in Alaska in 1938, the National Resources Committee reported to Congress that "the fisheries present a brilliant example of a successful conservation policy. Not so long ago it was feared that overfishing was threatening to ruin the industry. Today, the annual pack is greater than ever."[43] Occasionally a statement of emphatic dissent from a fisherman or someone close to the actual scene filtered upward to the Washington level, but these had little impact in contrast to the aforementioned pronouncements.

While practically all fishermen and labor groups were drawn into a cohesive unit in opposing the industry and the bureau on the trap issue, there was a great cleavage among their ranks which produced a different set of group alignments and greatly weakened labor's over-all political effectiveness. The issue in conflict was the question of the rights of employment in the fishery as between residents and nonresidents. Prior to the 1930s, the canners relied heavily upon nonresident fishermen and cannery workers because it was more economically expedient to do so. During the labor movement in the early 1930s, both resident and nonresident fishermen and workers were organized into the same international unions with headquarters in Seattle and San Francisco. Control of these unions rested with the numerically larger nonresident members who sought to maintain their dominance even though the conditions from which this situation originally stemmed were rapidly changing in Alaska.

As an example, for many years the Alaska Fishermen's Union

[41] *Ibid.*, p. 22.

[42] U.S. Department of the Interior, *Annual Report of the Governor of Alaska, 1936* (Washington: U.S. Government Printing Office, 1937), p. 1.

[43] National Resources Committee, *Regional Planning, Part IV, Alaska, Its Resources and Development* (Washington: U.S. Government Printing Office, 1938), p. 26.

with headquarters in San Francisco insisted that the canners pay the nonresident fisherman four cents more per fish than was paid to the resident member of the union. Other union contracts drawn up in San Francisco provided that the first six and one-half boats to every line of cannery machinery in the Bristol Bay region had to be manned by "outside" fishermen (i.e., thirteen nonresident fishermen per line of cannery machinery before a resident fisherman could be hired). In certain years this meant that a great number of resident fishermen, many with families to support in the area, were left on the beach without a job while the fishing was done by nonresidents.[44] As the conflict sharpened, relations between the two groups became extremely turbulent. The secretary of the Alaska Fishermen's Union, George Lane, served notice that "if the Alaska Fishermen's Union is expected to permit Alaskan residents to usurp their just proportion of jobs from the men in the States we will refuse to permit any fishing in the area."[45]

To the growing population of Alaska, struggling to develop and settle the territory at odds already made difficult by the natural environment, these and similar tactics by the unions represented further evidence of the evils of "absenteeism." A number of new unions composed entirely of Alaska resident fishermen and cannery workers were formed to try and break the hold of these powerful nonresident controlled unions, but they ran into many difficulties in gaining recognition by the industry for the purposes of bargaining and labor negotiations. Delegate Dimond introduced various bills in the House to provide for gradually increasing quotas of residents on the fishing grounds and in the canneries,[46] but he succeeded in getting only one minor piece of legislation through Congress, which provided that the insignificant set-net fishery in Bristol Bay was to be handled only by those who had resided in the area for two years.[47]

The packers were accused by some of holding out a helping hand to the nonresident labor groups in an effort to keep the

---

[44] These and other examples are thoroughly covered in: Gruening, *op. cit.*, pp. 385-391.

[45] Quoted in: Gruening, *op. cit.*, p. 289.

[46] For instance: H.R. 7987, H.R. 7988, and H.R. 8115, among others.

[47] 52 Stat. 208, April 7, 1938.

territory in its colonial status. Others charged that the industry was doing everything it could to increase the friction between the two factions in order to weaken labor's organized potency on other matters.

Out of this milieu there developed an extremely hostile attitude among many of the residents of Alaska toward absentee labor, absentee capital, and absentee government. The conviction began to take hold that these absentee groups were working collusively to prevent the territory from obtaining its just rewards from the region's most important industry—the salmon fishery. It was only a short step from this viewpoint to the conclusion that the situation could be effectively rectified only through full statehood along with complete control of the fisheries. In this way the administration of the salmon fishery became a burning political issue in the drive for statehood that gained momentum in the territory in the early 1940s.

Before the decade of the thirties was over, however, three events occurred which had a significant impact on the administration of the Alaska salmon fisheries. First, early in January of 1939 President Roosevelt accepted the resignation of Frank Bell as Commissioner of Fisheries at a time when Bell's regulatory policies in the Alaska salmon fishery were under their strongest attack from nearly every quarter. Second, under a Presidential Reorganization Plan approved by Congress in May 1939, the Bureau of Fisheries was transferred from the Department of Commerce to the Department of the Interior and early the next year was merged with the Bureau of Biological Survey, an agency for the preservation of wildlife,[48] to form the Fish and Wildlife Service.[49] Third, in July of 1939 Delegate Dimond succeeded in getting a resolution passed in the House of Representatives calling for a full congressional investigation of the administration of the Alaska salmon fisheries.[50] Beginning in the late summer a subcommittee of seven members of the House Merchant Marine and Fisheries Committee, headed by Chairman S. O. Bland of Virginia, held extensive hearings throughout Alaska and in Seattle

[48] It was formerly in the Department of Agriculture.

[49] U.S. Department of the Interior, *Annual Report of the Secretary*, 1940 (Washington: U.S. Government Printing Office, 1941), p. 291.

[50] H. Res. 162, passed July 17, 1939 (76th Cong., 1st Sess.)

and Washington, D. C.[51] The subcommittee was accompanied by a joint committee of four members from the Alaska territorial legislature and a number of bureau officials. The group traveled over 3,700 miles, heard 164 witnesses at the various hearings, and received depositions, affidavits and briefs from many others, all of which filled over one thousand pages of printed testimony. The congressmen visited all the major coastal cities in Alaska, saw canneries in operation, inspected fixed and floating traps, saw the various types of fishing gear in operation, witnessed salmon on the way to the spawning grounds, and conferred extensively with fishermen and cannery operators. It was one of the most comprehensive inquiries ever made by a congressional committee into the problems of the Alaska salmon fishery.

The hearings were mostly repetitive of testimony previously presented. However, the viewpoints of the Alaska residents were brought out more coherently and forcefully than they had ever been before, and the hearings as a whole provide evidence of the chaos existing in the fishery at the end of the decade.

The long-standing demand for the abolition of salmon traps was vigorously presented by many groups and likewise was strongly opposed by the packers. Over 75 per cent of the subcommittee's time was consumed on this question alone. The inability of the Alaska fishermen to make an adequate living was thoroughly aired, along with other aspects of the resident–nonresident conflict. Many of the fishermen admitted freely that a large part of their catch was taken illegally either from the mouths of spawning streams or pilfered from traps because of their desperate plight. There was widespread complaint of the Bureau of Fisheries administration for some years past. It was repeatedly charged that trap sites had been obtained through political favor or other improper methods and that the regulations had been the subject of political juggling and manipulation by certain favored packers, especially in the designation of areas to be opened or closed to fishing. The bureau was censored widely for laxity in law enforcement and for its neglect of biological research. Conflicting views were expressed on whether the salmon

[51] U.S. Congress, House, Committee on Merchant Marine and Fisheries, *Committee Study Resolution—Alaska Fisheries Hearings . . . Pursuant to H.R. 162,* 76th Cong., 1st Sess., 1939, Part I to IV, 1136 pp.

runs were being depleted, but generally the fishermen held that serious depletion was occurring in numerous areas (in their view owing primarily to the existence of traps), while the packers and the bureau denied there was evidence of depletion except perhaps in a few minor instances.

The subcommittee's report[52] was the subject of criticism from all sides. Great hope had been held in the territory that the congressional investigation would result in immediate legislative action to correct the policies, program, and administrative organization of the bureau along the lines that had been indicated in the hearing. To these people the report did not go nearly far enough.[53] To the packers and, to a lesser extent the nonresident labor groups, it was feared that the subcommittee had gone much too far in certain directions.

The single most important concept permeating the report[54] was summarized in these clear-cut terms:

> The fisheries of Alaska should be administered by the United States not solely for the purpose of conservation as contended by some, but also as an Alaskan resource to be administered, controlled, regulated and operated in the interest of and for the benefit of the Alaskan people.
>
> Your committee feels that the problem of the fishermen must be considered by the administrative agency along with conservation of the natural resource.[55]

The subcommittee was strongly impressed by the antitrap arguments, but did not make any specific recommendations for abolishment on the belief that there should be a complete study of the pattern of ownership, extent of monopoly, and the biological effects of traps in order to clear away the fog before any legislative action was attempted. On the basis of the evidence at hand, however, the subcommittee did say that traps had reached their peak in number; that they should not be increased; that very

---

[52] U.S. Congress, House, Merchant Marine and Fisheries Committee, *Investigations of Fisheries of Alaska, Preliminary Report Pursuant to H. Res. 162,* 76 Cong., 3rd Sess., 1940, 54 pp. (H. Report 2379).

[53] See for instance Gruening's criticism of the report on these grounds: Gruening, *op. cit.*, pp. 557-558.

[54] House Report 2379, 76 Cong., 3rd Sess., was printed in full in: U.S. Congress, House, Merchant Marine and Fisheries Committee, *Alaskan Fisheries. Hearings . . . Pursuant to H. Res.* 38, 79th Cong., 2nd Sess., 1946, pp. 71-113. (It is the source used here.)

[55] *Ibid.*, p. 101.

probably they should be reduced and redistributed; and that appropriate regulations might be required to control the capacity of each individual trap. It was recommended that all dummy traps be removed; that trap sites should not be assignable or transferable; and that traps should be closed and removed immediately for failure to obey the law. Finally, it was recommended that in studying the question of trap removal, the administrative agency should give consideration to conservation *and* to the effect of such elimination upon the earnings and livelihood of the fishermen.[56]

On the problem of resident *versus* nonresident labor, the subcommittee expressed sympathy with the hope that ultimately all fishery operations in the territory would be performed by Alaskans, but it was unable to see how this could be immediately attained without a considerable curtailment of activity. The point was made that the question of labor was closely interwoven with the trap-elimination question and that the two problems should be handled jointly. The idea of nonresident labor quotas to be fixed by the Secretary of the Interior was suggested, but it was concluded that before any administrative or legislative action was attempted every effort should be made to work out a satisfactory settlement by negotiation so that the residents would obtain a fair and just proportion of the work.[57]

The subcommittee disapproved of the bureau's past practice of holding its annual regulatory hearings only in Seattle and Washington, D. C. It strongly recommended that similar hearings be held in Alaskan communities so that residents would also have an opportunity to express their views. It was recommended that in order for bureau employees to become more familiar with conditions in the territory, the Alaska headquarters of the bureau be moved from Seattle to Juneau to bring the officers charged with the administration of the Alaska fisheries close to the field of operation.

The vastness of the Territory, the unforeseen changes in climatic and other conditions, unexpected problems, the importance of prompt decisions based upon facts obtained on the ground, make it almost impossible for any man or set of men to handle complicated matters

[56] *Ibid.*, p. 101.
[57] *Ibid.*, pp. 102-104.

like the Alaska fisheries when its headquarters are several thousand miles distant.[58]

Considerable emphasis was given to the need for a much more liberal appropriation for scientific research and for the administration and regulation of the Alaska fisheries. Many of the failures and mistakes of the bureau in the past could be traced very largely to the lack of funds and personnel. Specifically, it was noted that funds for enforcement of regulations in recent years had permitted only twelve permanent law enforcement officers to supervise and patrol over 10,000 miles of coastline; that there were only one hundred temporary seasonal stream guards in 1939 compared with over two hundred such employees in the years prior to 1933; and that British Columbia with less than half the coastline was spending over twice the amount spent in Alaska for enforcement work (i.e., in 1939 about $500,000 in British Columbia compared with $223,000 in Alaska).

As to scientific investigations, it was concluded that personnel and funds had been so limited and the points under observation so few that management of the salmon fisheries had been largely a matter of trial and error. Four employees located at the Seattle laboratory represented the entire scientific field force to cover the Alaska coastline. One of the outstanding weaknesses, it was revealed, was the present inability to measure with any reasonable accuracy the size of the spawning escapements of salmon to the rivers.[59] Attention was called to the complete lack of knowledge about the life and habits of the salmon while in their ocean habitat, and it was recommended that extensive offshore investigations be undertaken to provide the information needed.

The subcommittee noted the extreme divergence of opinions on the question of conservation *versus* depletion, and called attention to the lack of adequate scientific information on many aspects of the problem, upon which the administering agency could base accurate decisions. While the subcommittee did not voice a strong opinion one way or another on this question, it did conclude that the penny-wise, pound-foolish policy of the past must be overcome or "we soon will be looking on a vanishing resource."[60]

[58] *Ibid.*, p. 108.
[59] *Ibid.*, p. 111.
[60] *Ibid.*, p. 109.

Alaska Department of Fish & Game

Some of the 220 modern seine boats that waited for the opening of the 1956 pink salmon season at Anạn Creek in Southeast Alaska. Massive concentrations of fishing gear became an unmanageable problem as the the resource declined.

Unfortunately, by the end of the decade, fifteen years after passage of the celebrated White Act, the resource had been exploited so fully and relentlessly that depletion had reached a point where the total annual packs were falling alarmingly. Yet neither Congress, nor the bureau, nor for the most part those who were exploiting the resource were aware or cared to admit that such a serious condition existed. The intensity of fishing effort showed every sign of increasing, as did the clamor among the interest groups seeking to increase their share of the annual harvest from a waning resource.

7 *The Politics of Depletion*

THE NEWLY CREATED Fish and Wildlife Service in the Department of the Interior adopted the practice of holding annual hearings after each fishing season to determine the desirability, feasibility, and need for changes in the Alaska fishery regulations for the coming year. Hearings were held first in the fall of the year in the various fishing districts of Alaska to allow the residents a chance to express their views, and these were followed by hearings in Seattle where the packers, union officials, and other nonresident interest groups were given the opportunity to speak their piece. The regulatory changes for the coming year were generally announced sometime in early spring. A great deal of importance was given to these annual hearings by the government, and frequently the director of the Fish and Wildlife Service or one of his immediate assistants in commercial fisheries was on hand to conduct the hearings.

When this procedure was first adopted, the Service hoped all too idealistically that the hearings would allow the interested parties to participate and cooperate with the government in jointly hammering out annual regulations that not only would assure the proper escapement of salmon to the spawning grounds but would be in the best interest of the industry as a whole. However, given the economic forces operating in the declining fishery and the fierce conflicts of interests that had developed among the various groups exploiting the resource, it is not surprising that the annual hearings degenerated into pitched battles in which the government was constantly on the defensive.

With the approach of World War II the outlook for increased demand for canned salmon was exceptionally favorable, and as the price of the product began to rise, every government proposal to limit or even stabilize fishing pressures came under violent attack from those who would be adversely influenced. Groups that normally were at each other's throats on certain issues frequently found no difficulty in making expedient alignments in opposition to government proposals which might reduce their respective cuts of the pie. For example, beginning in 1941 the packers and the nonresident labor organizations agreed to hold joint meetings prior to the Seattle hearings to develop a unified and coordinated opposition to those proposed regulations which they agreed would be harmful to their mutual interests. In addition, the packers adopted the standard practice of going East each winter to the National Canners Convention which was held shortly after the Seattle hearings. Following the convention, a large, well-organized contingent of canners would proceed to Washington, D. C. to seek final modifications in the regulations. In this endeavor the Alaska packers had the support of the lobbyists for the National Fisheries Institute and the National Canners Association with permanent offices and staff at the Capital, as well as other friends of the industry in Congress and elsewhere.

That the government was feeling the full force of these pressures was brought out cogently in a speech delivered by the first director of the Fish and Wildlife Service at the Seattle hearings in 1941. The director, Dr. Ira N. Gabrielson, told the industry that the government was in the anomalous position of having to resist all pressures the industry could devise in order to prevent them from ruining their own business and livelihood. He concluded:

> And yet, year after year, the same groups in the same districts urge greater harvests—sometimes advancing one reason and sometimes another. There is little possibility that the conditions of any run are always so good as to justify greater harvests. One is therefore forced to conclude that the governing motive is the desire to take as many fish as possible *now* without any regard to the future supply.

No industry, no matter how potentially profitable it may be, can long endure if all the partners engage in indiscriminate looting.[1]

The director pointed out that the packers had a joint responsibility with the government in problems of law observance. "It seems," he said, "that intelligent self-interest would prevent any packer from encouraging law violations or from buying fish illegally taken, and yet both practices are followed too often."[2]

Neither caustic statements nor earnest entreaties from government officials had any effect upon the course of events, and as the annual packs dwindled and price of the product rose, the pressures upon the regulatory agency became more intense, emphatic, and unsavory. One pretext after another was found to justify the need for a relaxed regulatory program for the coming season. Beginning in 1942 it was the "war effort" that became the theme of the canners, and the new advertising slogan for canned salmon adopted shortly after Pearl Harbor was "food fit for MacArthur's men."[3]

The trade journal proclaimed that if the packers' necessities were presented strongly enough to the proper officials, the government probably would do everything possible to facilitate maximum production of salmon.[4] As a result, from 1942 through 1945 the Secretary of the Interior was prevailed upon to extend seasons, open previously closed areas to fishing, reduce or eliminate closed periods, and otherwise to progressively relax restrictions. When the War Production Board took steps to bring about a concentration of operations as a means of cutting down on materials and manpower needed for the war, the canned-salmon industry successfully prevailed upon the Secretary to liberalize the regulations even further to permit more fishing as a compensation for curtailment of operations. Yet curtailment in such an overcapitalized industry did not materially decrease the real productive potential sufficiently to warrant less restrictive regulations, and so the over-all result was an even greater intensity of fishing effort masquerading under the "war effort." No concern was exhibited by the packers over the possible effects this would have upon an already declining resource. Fortunately the Office of Price Administration was successful in preventing any

---

[1] *Pacific Fisherman*, December 1941, p. 48.
[2] *Ibid.*, p. 48.
[3] *Ibid.*, April 1942, p. 14.
[4] *Ibid.*, January 1942, p. 11.

sharp rises in the price of canned salmon during the war years, or otherwise the extent of the overexploitation would have been more severe than it was.

Following the war the market price of canned salmon did not fall as it had after World War I. Consequently there was no period similar to that of the early 1920s when the industry sought desperately to curtail production on its own accord. On the contrary, with the removal of wartime restrictions, the price of canned salmon began to increase at a rapid rate and the industry quickly began preparations to resume prewar packing operations in spite of the condition of the resource.

When the Secretary of the Interior proposed drastic regulations in 1946 to increase restrictions on fishing intensity with special emphasis on the trap, a great cry of anguish arose from the industry. The packers pointed out in a letter to the Secretary that such regulations would only add confusion and chaos to an already difficult operating situation as the industry sought to rehabilitate its facilities in preparations for "normal" operations. The Secretary was told that such regulations would wipe out millions of dollars of investment, bankrupt the territory and retard its postwar development and statehood, and that hundreds of returning veterans would be deprived of needed employment. Finally, it was said that such regulations would invariably lead to curtailment of production of a vitally important protein food during a period of acute world food shortage. This latter claim undoubtedly was motivated by a desire to find some theme to substitute for the "war effort" which had been so effective in the past, for it is difficult to believe that the canned-salmon industry was genuinely concerned over world hunger and starvation. Nothing was said in the letter about the high expectations for profits induced by rising prices.[5]

In response to pressures from the canners, several Fish and Wildlife Service officials went to Seattle from Washington, D. C., to discuss the proposed Alaska regulations for 1946. At the meeting the canners pressed for more "flexibility" in the setting of regulations which meant that field employees of the Service would be allowed to make decisions in the field based on day to day observations of the runs as to the need for restrictions. While there were good reasons for adopting such a flexible policy, it also meant that

[5] *Ibid.*, April 1946, p. 27.

many crucial decisions involving hundreds of thousands of dollars would be shifted to a single local employee in each region who would be vulnerable to pressures from the industry. The packers also pressed for a relaxation of the drastic limitations which the Secretary had proposed for the Bristol Bay area owing to the poor conditions of the runs there. In behalf of the packers it was pointed out at the meeting that owing to the war only half of the canneries in that region had been operated since 1941, and there had been nothing like "full-scale" operations since 1939. According to the packers, if they were to continue in business and maintain their plants, a good number of these idle canneries would have to resume operations that year. This meant that more gear would have to be allowed. Furthermore, it was pointed out that such action appeared especially desirable since a good run was in prospect for the following year and this would give them a chance to "iron the kinks out of the plants and get their crews and facilities reorganized" in preparation for full-scale operations in 1947.[6]

Following the meeting it was reported in the trade journal that most of the controversial points had been ironed out and an understanding reached which "should serve the needs of conservation without undue hardship to the industry,"[7] and when the final regulations were announced in the following month they contained all the major revisions requested by the packers.

In spite of these concessions, the 1946 season proved to be a failure throughout Alaska. The worst season in nineteen years, reported the trade journal in October, saved from being more severe only through the extension of the seasons in southeast Alaska by field announcements.[8] Fish were indeed becoming scarce.

There was no noticeable change in the attitudes and activities of the packers. Plans and preparations went ahead for the 1947 season as if nothing had happened. Prior to the Seattle hearings on the regulations, the industry met as usual and developed a clear-cut presentation. One of the main spokesmen named by the industry to present their case at the hearings was J. Steele Culbertson who had recently resigned as the chief fishery managment supervisor for the Fish and Wildlife Service in Alaska to join the staff of the Alaska

---

[6] *Ibid.*, March 1946, p. 53.
[7] *Ibid.*, p. 53.
[8] *Ibid.*, October 1946, p. 27.

Canned Salmon Industry, Inc., as assistant manager to W. C. Arnold. Culbertson was regarded by the industry as eminently qualified for the post "having become thoroughly acquainted with Alaska fishery matters through some fourteen years association with the Fish and Wildlife Service in the territory."[9] He introduced a new tactic which apparently reflected his understanding of these matters.

At the beginning of the hearings, Service officials announced a number of proposed changes looking toward more effective protection of the resource, including added restrictions on certain seine gear, increased closed areas, elimination of fall fishing, later seasonal openings in southeast Alaska, and increased closed periods and a large reduction of gear in Bristol Bay. The industry spokesman took the position that no such drastic restrictions were needed. All that was required was more effective policing and enforcement of present regulations by the Service. He pledged that the canned-salmon industry would coordinate all its powerful organizational machinery to assist the Service in gaining more funds from Congress for research, protection, regulation, and enforcement in the Alaska fisheries. This seemed a highly constructive approach. It was common knowledge that the Service had never been able to obtain the funds it needed to meet its responsibilities in Alaska, and the situation had become even more critical during the postwar years as the intensity of the fishery increased and appropriations remained relatively constant. But underneath the surface the industry proposal had characteristics of a bribe, for the packers seemed to be offering this support *if* the Service agreed that increased restrictions would not be necessary.

That the Service was attracted by the proposal was indicated in a

---

[9] *Ibid.*, March 1946, p. 37. (The movement of key personnel from the ranks of the federal government to the employ of the Alaska packers or their organizations occurred periodically throughout the history of the management of the fishery and may be indicative of a lack of dedication and *esprit de corps* exhibited by other federal agencies such as the Forest Service. Perhaps the most celebrated case was that of Jefferson F. Moser around the turn of the century. Moser had written a number of authoritative reports for the U.S. Fish Commission on the Alaska salmon fishery which were highly critical of the packers and their methods of exploitation. Later he was employed by the Alaska Packers Association at a high level, and he represented that organization as a lobbyist at many congressional hearings over the years at which he completely contradicted or reversed his earlier statements based on what he called "more mature" judgments.) This is detailed in Gruening, *op. cit.*, pp. 252-259.

statement made by the Assistant Director immediately following the hearings when he told the canners at their annual convention that "the present emergency calls for nothing radical or revolutionary but simply doing the job more effectively."[10] And it became overtly evident by the announcement of the final regulations which, in the words of the trade journal, contained few of the radical provisions discussed in hearings last fall, but instead followed a number of the recommendations offered by the operators.[11]

Again, in spite of the liberal terms of the regulations, the Alaska salmon pack was a miserable failure in 1947. The southeast Alaska pack was the poorest on record, even with numerous field extensions of the season. And so the process of depletion continued. Obviously the packers were motivated by the size of the profits, and these were most assuredly showing notable gains. For example, in 1947 the Pacific American Fisheries Company recorded a net profit of $1,844,340 and the Alaska Packers Association had an operating revenue from sales of salmon of $17,351,075 and a net profit of $3,207,784 in spite of the scarcity of fish and what was considered high operating costs.[12]

By the late 1940s, after a series of years in which the total Alaska salmon packs had been recorded as miserable failures, a glimmering of concern as to the future of the fishery began to develop among the packers. This did not spring forth on its own merit through a genuine anxiety over the state of the resource, but was the offspring of specific economic forces. The packers were beginning to worry whether the price of canned salmon could possibly continue the steep upward trend that had set in following the war. There were many uncertainties as to whether the retail and wholesale trade would continue to react favorably to increasingly higher salmon prices and scarcity of product. One major salmon broker noted with alarm that "salmon prices are so high . . . as almost to take it out of the staple class and put it beyond the average reach of the consumer." He noted that both retailers and consumers were beginning to buy on a hand-to-mouth basis rather than stocking up on the product as they had generally done in the past.[13] In addition, tuna,

---

[10] *Ibid.*, December 1946, p. 27.
[11] *Ibid.*, February 1947, p. 17.
[12] *Ibid.*, July 1948, pp. 57, 69.
[13] *Ibid.*, October 1948, p. 41.

one of the main market competitors for salmon, was rapidly increasing in volume and decreasing in price and the packers feared that if these trends continued tuna would soon take the place of salmon as a staple.

But the prices of all species of canned salmon continued to rise in spite of these concerns, and with the coming of the Korean War in the early 1950s the market for canned salmon received an additional boost. Nevertheless, the mere existence of these fears had an effect upon the packers' attitudes. For the first time in many years the subject of conservation began to receive some attention at the annual meetings and conventions of the packers.

Outstanding was a new emphasis on the importance of scientific research and the need to increase the knowledge necessary in forming regulations. It was noted at a meeting of the packers, for instance, that while the Fish and Wildlife Service had made some progress in its Alaska research, knowledge of the fish was not yet sufficient to form a thoroughly solid basis for regulation and the government was merely feeling its way along on a trial-and-error basis with no positive proof to support its contentions. One of the main points of controversy at the time revolved around the so-called late pink salmon runs in southeast Alaska. The Service was contending that the season in this area needed to be shortened owing to the poor condition of the runs, while the industry was contending that important late runs had built up over the years which could be harvested properly only if the season was extended.

As a result of this seemingly new interest in conservation and the existence of disagreement over scientific facts, the industry decided to establish its own research program to consider vital biological problems of the Alaska salmon. In the late 1940s the University of Washington approved a proposal by the Alaska Salmon Industry, Inc., which led to the establishment of the Fisheries Research Institute at the University to undertake an industry-sponsored program of intensified research. The first project centered around the controversy over the pink salmon runs in southeast Alaska, and each of the packers in that area pledged two cents per case of their total output to support the research. The program proved successful from the very beginning and it was rapidly expanded in both scope and magnitude in succeeding years.

The move to establish an industry-sponsored biological research program was hailed in the trade journal as one of the most constructive acts ever undertaken by the industry. It was said by the first director of the program, Dr. W. F. Thompson, to mark the passing of an old attitude in which conservation regulations were passively accepted by men interested solely in carrying exploitation as far as the law would allow, and that it represented a recognition among the packers for the first time that "conservation is good business."[14]

Unfortunately, such a naïve view was not warranted. While the scientific investigations carried out by the Institute were of high calibre and the establishment of the program represented an important step in the right direction, it was not the result of any basic metamorphosis in either the attitudes or the activities of the packers. On the contrary, fights over the annual regulations became, if anything, even more tempestuous. Furthermore, there were certain side-effects, perhaps partly unavoidable, that were not altogether salubrious.

Within a very short time the funds expended by industry for biological research exceeded those spent by the federal government. This resulted in a situation in which the regulating agency, in the process of setting policy, frequently was obliged to rely upon the scientific findings produced by those who were being regulated. Regardless of the merit of the research, this was not a particularly healthy position for the federal agency. Furthermore, there was a tendency in the industry-sponsored program to emphasize the role of natural factors as causes of the fluctuation in the abundance of salmon. For instance, when the first results of the program were announced in 1950 at a conference of salmon canners, it was concluded that all data on southeast Alaska indicated "some other factor than the fishery" was mainly responsible for the decreasing abundance "leading to the question of whether physical conditions may be the determining factor."[15] Heavy losses to escapement caused by natural predators such as gulls, bear, and beluga whale, and the adverse effects of "overcrowding of spawning streams" were stressed along with other natural factors. Nothing at all was mentioned to indicate that Man, the most efficient of all predators of the salmon, might be exploiting the resource too intensely. Perhaps this was too

[14] *Ibid.*, March 1947, p. 23. (Quotation from a paper delivered by Dr. W. F. Thompson entitled, "The Hand of Industry in Conservation Research.")

[15] *Ibid.*, April 1950, p. 17.

U.S. Fish & Wildlife Service

During the summer, bears feed upon the hordes of salmon on their way to the spawning beds. Here is a choice spot on McNeil Creek near Kamishak Bay. Flocks of gulls along the spawning streams are characteristic sights.

Jack H. Helle

An agile black bear plunges his nose into the cold water and comes up with a struggling chum salmon.

simple to warrant mention. At any rate, following the conference the industry trade journal reported that the packers were enthusiastically convinced of the worthwhile character of the research program from "a hard-boiled, dollars-and-cents standpoint."[16]

The industry-sponsored program also tended to act as a palliative for the individual packer who could rationalize that his annual payment to support scientific research not only was tangible proof of his deep interest in conservation, but absolved him of any further personal responsibility toward the resource in the conduct of his operations. Closely related to this was the emergence of an exaggerated reliance upon "science" (referring to greater biological knowledge) as a panacea for the complicated ills that besieged the industry, many of which were of economic, social, or political origin. It was frequently pointed out in the trade journal and elsewhere that "science" had solved many problems in recent years and that "science" could do it again in the case of the Alaska salmon. All that was needed was more biological knowledge.

The biologists, ichthyologists, and other fishery scientists—both government and industry employed—did much to perpetrate this fallacious impression through frequent statements intimating that if they only had more money for scientific research (and perhaps more control over policy formation—usually stated in terms of removing it from "politics"), they could solve the problems of conserving the salmon.

True, there existed a shocking need for greater knowledge upon which to base a sound regulatory program, but this new emphasis ignored the importance of understanding the human predator and the need to find more effective means to control and direct his activities toward socially desirable ends. As in the case of the misguided reliance upon hatcheries in earlier years, it created a false impression among the packers that through "science" they could continue to have their cake and eat it too.

Prices of canned salmon continued to increase and so did the intensity of exploitation. At the end of the decade it was noted in the annual report of the Secretary of the Interior that

> the year 1949 set a new record for the number of boats and units of gear operating in Alaska. Never in the history of the Territory has

---

[16] *Ibid.*, p. 17.

exploitation of the fisheries been so intense, and never has the need been so great for vigorously enforced, sound regulatory controls.[17]

It was not only a problem of the amount of gear that plagued the fishery. As the Service continued to shorten the seasons in an effort to reduce fishing pressures at particular locations, mobile gear began to shift from one fishing area to another as the seasons were opened and closed. This resulted in massive concentrations of gear at points where and when it could be most effective. Each individual salmon became so valuable that creek robbing, poaching, and other violations of the regulations developed into a tremendous enforcement problem which the federal service, with its meager funds and personnel, was utterly unable to control. Furthermore, the economic impetus to violate the law was augmented by the existence of traps. As Dr. Rogers pointed out in his study:

> As a full load of salmon was being brailed [from the trap] into the cannery scow, a passing fisherman could compare this sight with his empty or partially filled hold and reflect that there but for the grace of an infernal machine and its distant owners went the fish he might have caught and sold to meet the mortgage payments on his boat and gear and pay the family's grocery bill.[18]

To the ordinary fishermen, this seemed proof enough that the federal government was in league with the cannery people. Why should he obey the law, he could rationalize, when that same law allowed the absentee interests to rob the country legally at his expense?

Various attempts were made during the 1940s to get legislation through Congress giving the Secretary of the Interior the much needed authority to control the amount of gear in the fishery, but these became hopelessly entangled with other controversial issues. For example, in the early 1940s shortly after the Bureau of Fisheries was transferred to the Interior, officials of the Fish and Wildlife Service began working on a new Alaska Fishery Law designed to supersede the White Act. Instead of accepting fishery operations as a public right or universal privilege, the new approach proposed to prohibit all fishing and canning in Alaska *except* as expressly permitted by the Secretary. All fishermen and operators would be

[17] U.S. Department of the Interior, *Annual Report of the Secretary,* 1949 (Washington: U.S. Government Printing Office, 1950), p. 274.

[18] Rogers, *op. cit.,* p. 12.

required to obtain a license or permit and the Secretary could specify both the number and type of gear that could be employed in each fishing area. A rough draft of the proposal was submitted to the industry for study early in 1941 and various organizations were invited to send representatives to Washington, D. C. to discuss the bill in conference with Service officials. While there appeared

Alaska Historical Museum

The majority of fish traps were owned by cannery operators and other "absentee interests." To Alaskans the controversial trap became the symbol of outside exploitation of this fishery resource; such traps were not prohibited until Alaska achieved statehood in 1958.

to be a general realization in the industry of the need to control the amount of gear, the proposed bill contained features considered objectionable by the interest groups, and efforts at the meeting to reconcile conflicting views and bring out a proposal satisfactory to all did not succeed.[19]

Instead, later in the year Senator Wallgren of Washington introduced a bill (S. 1915) embodying the views of the packers,

[19] *Pacific Fisherman,* September 1941, p. 24.

the majority of whom were his constituents. The bill differed considerably from the original draft proposed by the Fish and Wildlife Service. Among the new features was a provision for the licensing of traps which would establish definite proprietary trap-fishing rights, with preferential rights going to the original holder of the site. The bill also provided for a Fishery Advisory Board composed of two industry and two labor representatives, and it included an elaborate and time-consuming procedure of hearings and review in order to change the regulations. The bill never got out of committee, and in the following session of Congress Senator Wallgren introduced a similar measure (S. 2227) which suffered the same fate. Early in 1943 the Senator introduced a revised version (S. 930) and hearings were held on the bill in Washington, D. C. by the Committee on Commerce, of which he was a member.

This new version not only contained most of the provisions in the earlier bills, but had been broadened considerably to cover other subjects besides that of controlling the amount of gear in the fishery. For one thing, it contained a provision to extend the jurisdiction of the United States to all waters east of the international boundary line between Russia and the United States, and to all waters less than 200 fathoms in depth. This amounted to a considerable extension beyond the historic three-mile limit and reflected a growing fear within the industry of a possible encroachment of Japanese and other foreign nationals upon the salmon fishery. Another new provision was that these waters would be open to all citizens of the United States "free of all exclusive or several rights of fishery under any claim of occupancy, aboriginal or otherwise."[20] This was designed specifically to divest the Indians and other aboriginal peoples of Alaska of certain claims to special rights and privileges in the fishery that were being forcefully pressed. The sections of the bill providing authority to control the amount of gear were modeled after the principle applied in the Taylor Grazing Act. All fishing activities were required to be licensed, and if restriction required that some users be forced out of the fishery, it was provided that "previous use and proximity" established a superior claim over newcomers or strangers.[21]

---

[20] S. 930, Section 2.

[21] U.S. Congress, Senate, Committee on Commerce, *Alaska Fisheries Act, Hearings . . . on* S. *930,* 78th Cong., 2nd Sess., 1944, pp. 1-5.

On hand at the Washington hearings to testify in favor of the bill were W. C. Arnold, director of Alaska Salmon Industry, Inc.; Ernest D. Clark representing the Association of Pacific Fisheries and the Northwest Salmon Canners' Association; Nick Bez, prominent Alaska salmon packer; F. J. Gunderson, independent trap owner; and Bjorne Halling of the CIO Maritime Committee, representing trap laborers.

Opposing the bill was Alaska's congressional delegate, Anthony Dimond, who objected on the grounds that it was designed at the behest of the industry "to erect the privilege of fishing with traps into vested rights."[22] The bill made certain, he said, that the trap owners would be able to occupy a piece of ground in the coastal waters of Alaska until Kingdom come. He noted bitterly that this was an Alaska fisheries bill and yet no one in Alaska had been consulted. Said the delegate:

> Nobody sent me a copy of the bill. I don't know anything about it. Nobody asked my opinion. Nobody requested me to come here. I had to find out myself in order to come over here and make my protest. . . . But I say to the committee that every fisherman in Alaska that I know is strongly, and some of them bitterly, opposed to the provisions of this bill principally because it will make a monopoly or tend to fasten upon the country irretrievably the monopoly which exists in the ownership and operation of traps—and they are against it.[23]

He was opposed to the provisions creating an advisory board which was to meet annually in Seattle, and to the stipulations regarding procedures for regulatory hearings. Concluded the delegate:

> I spoke a little while ago of absentee landlordism, and we have it with a vengeance in Alaska. I haven't any grievance against those who invest their money in Alaska or work in Alaska. God knows. But here we have a provision for hearings on the regulations, and that provision is that the hearings are to be held *where* to regulate the Alaska fisheries? They are to be held in Seattle, Washington. . . . We have fishermen in Alaska who cannot travel to Seattle. . . . The packers can more easily go to Juneau than the fishermen with their small income can come to Seattle. I think it is an outrage.[24]

Dr. Ira N. Gabrielson, director of the Fish and Wildlife Service, testified that while there were certain aspects of the bill needing

[22] *Ibid.*, p. 32.
[23] *Ibid.*, p. 38.
[24] *Ibid.*, pp. 40-42.

revision, the Service was in favor of the passage of this or some other legislation of a similar nature. He pointed out to the committee that the Service had little means to control the rapidly increasing fishing intensity except by shortening of the seasons and other methods of limited effectiveness, and he concluded that the Service was in dire need of the additional powers provided in the bill.[25]

While Dr. Gabrielson's testimony seemed to put the Service in the middle of the road on this particular bill, the committee received a lengthy letter from Abe Fortas, the Assistant Secretary of the Interior, which dealt the Wallgren bill a death blow.[26] The Assistant Secretary noted that while a substantial need existed for the general revision of the Alaska fishery laws, there nevertheless were so many objectionable and ambiguous features in the Wallgren bill that the department could not recommend passage unless it was extensively revised and amended. Five specific objections were discussed in detail. First, the extension of United States jurisdiction over fishing activities outside territorial water did not give due recognition to accepted principles of international law and would lead to greater jurisdictional conflict. Second, the regulatory measures were not sufficiently flexible or precise, and hampering and confusing procedural restrictions were imposed on the regulatory agency. Third, the plan for allocating fishing privileges contained features which would tend to promote the monopolization of the Alaska fisheries by a few large operators to the detriment of independent fishermen and the people of Alaska. Fourth, the bill would deprive the natives of Alaska of aboriginal rights antedating the establishment of commercial fishing in that region and on which they were largely dependent for their sustenance. And fifth, the bill did not meet the proposed purpose of consolidating all basic laws relating to the commercial fisheries of Alaska, but left the situation in a confusing state.

The Assistant Secretary presented the committee with a long list of amendments that would need adoption to make the bill acceptable to the department. Among those directly concerned with provisions to control the amount of gear, he called for the inclusion of a clause that no vested rights in the fishery would be created

[25] *Ibid.*, pp. 85-91.
[26] *Ibid.*, pp. 97-101. (Testimony of Abe Fortas.)

by the issuance of permits, licenses, and leases, and that all rights would be subject to the regulations promulgated by the Secretary. He said a "reasonable fee" should be paid to the government for any permits, licenses, or leases involving trap sites and other fishing rights, and he suggested that five criteria be substituted for the single criterion contained in the bill for the purpose of deciding who would get the individual allocations. These were: (1) prior rights to applicants who fished in any of the five years immediately preceding; (2) the preservation for native fishermen of the fishing privileges essential for earning a livelihood sufficient for their sustenance; (3) the provision for *bona-fide* residents of Alaska of equitable opportunities for participating in the utilization of the fishery resource; (4) that no person could lose his rights because of time spent in the armed forces; and (5) the avoidance of excessive concentrations of fishing privileges in the hands of a limited number of operators. In addition, he recommended that regulatory hearings be held in Alaska as well as in Seattle.

These recommendations would have completely thwarted the intended aim of the bill as originally conceived by the industry, and no attempt was made by the proponents to bring about a compromise over the controversial provisions. There was enough strength behind the bill to get it reported out of committee with a favorable recommendation, but without the backing of the Department of the Interior the bill was destined to follow the way of its two predecessors and it died without coming to a vote on the floor.

Another attempt to get Congress to provide the Service with authority to control the amount of gear came near the end of the decade as a direct outgrowth of the trap controversy. Throughout the forties, bills to outlaw traps had been introduced in virtually every session of Congress by the Alaska delegate. At the same time the trap-operating members of the industry, not being wholly certain of their trap control from year to year, had continually sought legislation to assure the permanence of this form of gear. None of these bills succeeded in getting very far in Congress, but in 1948 those who sought to have traps abolished were provided with a powerful new tool which brought the issue to a crucial juncture. Over the strenuous opposition of the canned-salmon lobby, the Eighteenth Territorial Legislature had succeeded in passing a bill providing for a territorial-wide referendum on the question of whether traps should be retained or abolished over a ten-year period, and the results reported following the general election in the fall of 1948 showed that the people of Alaska had voted 19,712 to 2,624 for trap abolition, a ratio of nearly eight to one.[27]

Armed with this strong evidence of the popular disapproval of the trap, the Alaska delegate promptly introduced a bill (H.R. 1515) in the next session of Congress conforming to the terms of the referendum, confident that in the face of this popular vote, the members of Congress would not delay any longer in passing the legislation.

Fish and Wildlife Service officials realized there was a good chance Congress would be inclined to act on the trap issue during the current session, and they saw in this a strategic opportunity to gain support behind a substitute measure that would allow the Service to regulate fishing intensity by all types of gear. Accordingly, a five-point proposal was quickly drafted by the Service and submitted to the industry with a request that they reply by airmail or telegram. As expected, the Alaska Canned Salmon Industry, Inc., responded that the packers would vigorously oppose any antitrap measure, but would offer no resistance to a proposal giving the Service greater control over gear through a licensing and leasing system.[28]

With this assurance the Service was ready to act. When hearings began a month later in Washington, D. C., on the delegate's trap-elimination measure, the Service immediately offered a substitute bill requiring permits for all fishing operations, and permitting the Secretary of the Interior to limit both the total catch and the amount of gear in any fishing area in Alaska as deemed necessary.[29] On the sensitive trap issue the substitute measure merely gave the Secretary the power to eliminate traps, but how or when to accomplish this was left for further study and consultation. According to the industry trade journal, this latter provision was offered as "bait" to the Alaskans in an effort to offset their expected opposition to other features of the proposed substitute.[30]

Congressional hearings were held at Seattle and various points

---

[27] *Session Laws of Alaska,* 1947, Chap. 2.

[28] *Pacific Fisherman,* January 1949, p. 1.

[29] U.S. Congress, House, Merchant Marine and Fisheries Committee, *Elimination of Salmon Traps in the Waters of Alaska, Hearings . . . on H.R. 1515,* 81st Cong., 1st Sess., 1949, pp. 2-18.

[30] *Pacific Fisherman,* May 1949, p. 51.

in Alaska during the fall of 1949.[31] The Service maintained that the elimination of fish traps provided no permanent solution to conserving the salmon because additional mobile-gear units would merely move in to take their place and eventually nullify any benefits which might accrue. The salmon packers maintained that the government should be allowed to control the number of units of all types of gear, but that trap elimination would be unjust and dis-

Alaska Department of Fish & Game

A modern cannery installation located on remote Naknek River, Bristol Bay. The fleet of boats tied to the cannery docks is owned by the canning company. Fishermen and cannery workers are flown to Bristol Bay from as far south as San Francisco to man this and similar plants in the region.

criminatory and had nothing whatever to do with conservation. The Alaska representatives maintained that the two questions were distinctly different, that Congress should act first on the people's overwhelming desire to abolish fish traps before considering the need to control the amount of gear, and that the substitute measure was injected primarily to undermine the original proposal by confusing the issues.

Although nearly a thousand pages of testimony were taken at the

[31] Hearings on H.R. 1515, *op. cit.*, 772 pp.

hearings on the controversial issues, the subcommittee was unable to come to any agreement. No report was ever issued in spite of the voluminous record, and what had become known as the "more power move" of the Fish and Wildlife Service failed completely. The substitute measure was never officially introduced in Congress and the delegate's original bill to eliminate fish traps died in committee. As a result, the status quo was maintained and the intensity of exploitation continued to increase as the fishery moved toward disaster in the 1950s.

One of the most conspicuous conflicts that developed during the 1940s involved the question of the social responsibilities of the Fish and Wildlife Service in the management of the Alaska salmon fishery. It will be recalled that during the 1930s an unsuccessful attempt was made for the first time in the history of federal management to bring the conservation program in line with broader goals and policies of the administration, and the decade ended with a congressional investigation by a House committee which praised these efforts and recommended that in the future much greater attention be given to important social and economic implications in the formulation and conduct of the regulatory program.

To understand what occurred during the forties it is necessary to realize the importance of the Interior Department's role in Alaska, for no other agency of government had such control and influence over Alaskan affairs. The Governor and the Secretary of the territory were employees of the department. Through its Bureau of Indian Affairs the department had exclusive jurisdiction over all programs relating to health, education, welfare, and economic development of Alaska's large Indian, Eskimo, and Aleut populations. The Office of the Territories whose prime function was to promote the economic, social, and political development of the nation's territorial possessions was also a branch of the department. Over 99 per cent of the vast land area of Alaska was under the jurisdiction of some federal agency, and by far the largest percentage of this was under the Bureau of Land Management within the department. Other natural-resource agencies in the department with important functions in the territory included the National Park Service, with large land holdings of its own, and the Geological Survey. When the Fish and Wildlife Service was added in 1940, the department's jurisdiction over Alaskan resources was increased to include all fish and game, both land and marine. With its numerous and varied functions and responsibilities in Alaska, it is not surprising that the Department of the Interior viewed the conservation of the salmon resource in a different perspective than it had been under the Department of Commerce.

It became evident in the early forties, for instance, that there were officials in high quarters within the department, including the Secretary, who believed that certain social goals should be maximized in the process of managing and conserving the salmon resource. Two specific social issues came to the front. One concerned the role of the native peoples of Alaska in the salmon fishery and the other involved the question of the effects of the pattern of trap ownership upon the economic development of the territory. It is not necessary for the purposes of this study to set out in detail the pros and cons of the tremendous controversy that was generated over the two issues during the period. Both Drs. George Rogers and Ernest Gruening have thoroughly analyzed these in their respective studies of Alaska.[32] It is important, however, to bring out a number of salient points which reveal the strongly negative attitude that existed within the Fish and Wildlife Service toward efforts within the department to meet what they considered were their social responsibilities.

The controversy erupted in 1942 with the issuance of two legal opinions by Nathan E. Margold, the Solicitor of the Department of the Interior dealing with Indian rights. In the first of these opinions it was concluded that aboriginal occupancy established possessory rights in Alaskan waters and submerged lands, and that such rights had not been extinguished by any treaty, statute, or administrative action by the federal government. In effect, the opinion opened the door to claims by coastal Indians of exclusive fishing rights over some of the most important fishing grounds in Alaska, including important trap fishing areas. This move by the department was part of a much broader crusade by the Bureau of Indian Affairs to improve the economic and social well-being of the Indian peoples and to re-establish something of their former culture through greater control over the land and marine resources which at one time had been in their possession.

The second Solicitor's opinion which followed a month later was

[32] See: Rogers, *op. cit.*, pp. 175-269; and Gruening, *op. cit.*, pp. 355-381.

designed to break the industry's near monopoly of the trap sites and to clear the way for a redistribution in ownership along lines considered by the department to be more equitable from a social and economic standpoint.[33] It was concluded in the opinion that the Secretary of the Interior had the legal authority to limit the number of traps that could be occupied by any individual, corpora-

U.S. Department of Fish & Game

Successful gillnet fishermen in Bristol Bay begin to untangle their huge catch of red salmon. In recent years fish have been so scarce that the average fisherman hardly makes expenses, but occasionally a massive run appears and an average fisherman stands to earn as much as $6,000 during the four-week fishing season.

tion, or combination, and to limit the amount of fish that could be taken by each. To the charge that this had nothing to do with conservation and hence was invalid under the White Act, the Solicitor said:

Underlying this argument is the assumption that an administrator charged with rule-making power under a statute is necessarily precluded

[33] The full text of the first opinion is found in *Hearings . . . on S. 2037 . . . and H.J. Res. 162, op. cit.*, pp. 415-426, and the second in *Hearings . . . on H. R. 38, op. cit.*, pp. 14-21.

from giving any weight to any consideration of public policy other than those expressly set forth in the statute. I find no warrant for any such assumption. If an administrator may achieve the declared statutory purpose of conservation through several alternative types of regulations, it is certainly appropriate for him to consider whether one type of regulation would be more expensive or less expensive to administer than another, or would have a more serious or less serious effect in disrupting existing transportation arrangements, or would result in a more equitable or less equitable distribution of fishing rights, even though none of these subsidiary factors be specifically mentioned.

The discretion which the statute here confers upon the Secretary to promulgate such regulations "as he may deem advisable" necessarily authorizes a consideration of all those factors which may, in the opinion of the Secretary, help to determine whether a particular mode of regulation is "advisable."

Therefore, I am constrained to hold that it is no valid objection to the proposed regulations that they may entail socially valuable consequences not expressly considered in the statute, such as the elimination of monopoly.[34]

The two opinions produced a violent reaction. Practically every element within the industry, except the Indians themselves, were indignantly opposed to the first opinion. On the second opinion the interest groups were divided on a resident–nonresident basis, with the packers and trap operators leading the opposition. During the next few years the Secretary attempted to move ahead along the lines originally outlined. In almost every case, however, these efforts were successfully thwarted and nothing concrete was accomplished toward the stated objectives.

Regardless of the merit of the arguments either for or against these particular issues, it became clear in the course of the battles that officials of the Fish and Wildlife Service were themselves resolutely opposed to any attempt, no matter from what origin, to broaden the concept of conservation to include the consideration of socially desirable ends. For example, at congressional hearings in 1949 concerning the trap issue, the chief counsel for the Fish and Wildlife Service stated frankly that the Service was interested in preserving the stock of fish and was not concerned with who caught the fish so long as there was sufficient brood stock left over to perpetuate the supply.[35] Later in the hearings the following ex-

[34] Hearings on H. Res. 38, *op. cit.*, pp. 14-21.
[35] Hearings on H. R. 1515, *op. cit.*, p. 15.

change took place between the Alaska congressional delegate and Seton H. Thompson, Chief of the Alaska Fisheries Branch, concerning this interpretation of the Service's responsibilities:

DELEGATE BARTLETT: From the conservation standpoint, then, as you see it, you would not care whether one individual or corporation caught all the fish in Alaska. Your only interest is in conserving the supply of fish, is that right?
THOMPSON: That is the way we interpret the statute that authorizes the regulation of the fisheries.
DELEGATE BARTLETT: In other words, the social and economic effects are not regarded by the Fish and Wildlife Service as its concern?
THOMPSON: That is our interpretation of our statute.[36]

A few years later the official view of the Service was summarized succinctly by Donald McKernan who was administrator of Alaska Commercial Fisheries at the time and later became director of the Bureau of Commercial Fisheries in Washington, D. C. In a similar discussion of the extent of the concept of fisheries management, McKernan said, "I believe it should be our job to conserve, manage and provide for the very maximum utilization of this resource and not [consider] the economic, social and political question as to who gets the fish."[37] Thus, the Service apparently sought to absolve itself of any responsibility for the social consequences of its actions by the simple expedient of defining its ultimate ends solely in biological terms.

This may have resulted in part from a belief that conflict could be avoided by ignoring it, but also it was a reflection of the scientific background of the chief administrators who were in full control of management policy within the Fish and Wildlife Service organization. It also reflected a great victory for the packers and other elements within the industry who had been pushing this "scientific" view since the 1930s in the full realization that an approach which considered the welfare of people as well as fish would undoubtedly lead to a change in the status quo which would not be beneficial to their interests. Ironically, while the canned-salmon industry pushed blatantly for a strictly biological approach to management of the fishery, they were not at all averse to combating

[36] *Ibid.*, p. 18.
[37] U.S. Congress, House, Committee on Territorial and Insular Affairs, *Hearings . . . Pursuant to H.R. 30,* 84th Cong., 1st Sess., Part IV, p. 143.

U.S. Fish & Wildlife Service

Weirs are constructed across selected streams each year, allowing biologists to make an accurate count of salmon escapement to the spawning beds. Here red salmon mill around the base of a weir at the outlet of Brooks Lake on the Alaska Peninsula.

"objectionable" regulations with arguments that such regulations would result in uneconomic operations, loss of investments, and other similar consequences of a strictly economic nature. The Fish and Wildlife Service seemed never to recognize the contradiction.

This approach to resource management contrasted sharply with that of the United States Forest Service in the Department of Agriculture, which controlled much of the forest resources along the Alaska coastline. In the early 1900s when the huge Tongass and Chugach national forests were created in Alaska, the Forest Service adopted and steadfastly applied a management philosophy which insisted on the use of these resources "in such a way that they will make the greatest contribution to the Territory's economy."[38] The policy explicitly recognized: (1) that it was in the public interest to foster the economic development of Alaska; (2) that increased economic development would have to come through industry based on such natural resources presently there; and (3) that one of the natural resources which could make a substantial contribution to stable industrial development of Alaska was the forest resource. In 1954 the Forest Service viewpoint of its responsibilities in Alaska was summarized by the Regional Forester in the following terms:

> The [resource management concept] must also recognize people, since the ultimate objective of managing forests is to make them serve people. Ordinarily, this human phase covers as a minimum the need for steady jobs and the varying degree of dependence of people and communities on the forests from which these jobs come.[39]

Obviously the two federal agencies viewed their respective responsibilities from different vantage points.

It may be questionable to carry this comparison further because of the different set of problems the two agencies faced. However, it should be noted that for decades the Forest Service fought strenuously in the face of severe and outspoken criticism to maintain policies which assured that the timber resources would not be logged from Alaska's shores and shipped to distant processing points outside the territory with little benefit to the local economy. Under these policies, timber-resource development progressed slowly until around the end of World War II when demand for forest products reached a point where it became economically feasible to establish large-scale pulp and other processing industries in Alaska. As a result, today the timber resources of Alaska support a healthy, growing industry which employs hundreds of people on a stable year-round basis representing one of the most important growth segments in the over-all Alaska economy.

The fisheries, on the other hand, followed an opposite trend, and as salmon depletion progressed in the forties and fifties the people

---

[38] Quoted from: *Timber Sales in Alaska* (multilithed statement distributed by Regional Office of U.S. Forest Service, Juneau), March 5, 1957.

[39] A. W. Greeley, "Applying the Working Circle Concept in Managing the Tongass National Forest" (typewritten copy of a paper presented at the Fifth Alaska Science Conference, Juneau), September 1954.

of Alaska suffered as that segment of their economy deteriorated. Fishermen and cannery workers were hard pressed by seasonal failures and the steady decline of the supply. Perhaps the most adversely affected were the coastal Indians because they had fewer off-season earning possibilities and had come to rely largely on the income during the fishing season for their year's livelihood. Their predicament was further altered for the worse by policies of the Bureau of Indian Affairs which committed the Indian loan program almost exclusively to the acquisition of bigger boats and more efficient gear, and the gradual acquisition of defunct private canneries by Indian communities at a time when the resource was rapidly declining.[40]

It was out of these worsening conditions in the territory that the conduct of the salmon fishery became a burning issue in the drive for statehood and full self-government. Dr. Ernest Gruening, who was appointed Governor of Alaska in 1939 by Franklin D. Roosevelt, was perhaps the man most responsible for stirring the people of Alaska to action, and in so doing he incurred the enmity of many persons in both government and industry who, for differing reasons of their own, wished to see no change whatever in the political status quo. Governor Gruening was a "new dealer," an intellectual, and an extremely astute and effective political leader. He had for the previous five years been director of the Division of Territories and Insular Affairs in the Department of the Interior. He was appalled at the economic, social, and political conditions he found in Alaska, and he pressed for what he considered necessary reforms. Among the most controversial of these were the various tax proposals he presented to the Alaska Territorial Legislature during the 1940s.

To fully understand what followed it is necessary to realize the powerful role the canned-salmon lobby played in the history of the Alaska legislature. Dr. George Rogers summarized the situation in the following terms:

> Because the natural resources they were engaged in exploiting were under the exclusive control of the federal government . . . they had nothing positive to ask of the territorial government. . . . The principals

---

[40] For a full discussion of this program and its effects on the Indians of southeast Alaska see: Rogers, *op. cit.*, pp. 221-269. Rogers also provides a superb comparative analysis on the Forest Service and Fish and Wildlife Service program in southeast Alaska in his chapter entitled, "Managing the Region's Resources," pp. 271-316.

of the lobby, with their largely imported seasonal labor forces and absentee capital, were indifferent to the adequacy of the territory's school system, and its public health and welfare services. Because their wealth was extracted from the natural wealth found within the borders of the territory, however, their income, products and property were legally open to taxation by this territorial government. They were vitally concerned indeed, therefore, with how much these community services cost and what form of taxation was used in paying for them.

The general aims of the lobby, therefore, were negative and obstructionist—defeat all measures which increase the cost of government, cut appropriations for existing services whenever possible, block all attempts to increase taxes or to reform the tax system by providing general net income or property taxes, kill any moves in the direction of Alaska's assuming more control of its natural resources. Rarely was the lobby interested in promoting any measure.[41]

Governor Gruening had been in office less than a year when he clashed head-on with the canned-salmon lobby. In his message to the Territorial Legislature in January, 1941, he proposed a program of tax revision designed to (1) distribute the burden fairly and in proportion to the ability to pay; (2) insure a dependable flow of revenue independent of fluctuations; (3) eliminate some of the injustices and inequities which now exist; (4) diminish some of the evils as the result of not controlling our absenteeism sufficiently; (5) rid Alaska business and professions of the so-called nuisance taxes; and (6) raise more revenue.[42]

There were various problems in connection with the taxation of the fisheries which the Governor sought to correct. Although the existing fisheries taxes were bringing in between 40 to 50 per cent of the total territorial revenue, this actually amounted to less than 2 per cent of the wholesale value of canned salmon produced in Alaska, and it was felt that the industry should bear a larger burden of the increasing costs of territorial government. Furthermore, the canners paid a tax based on the number of cases of canned salmon produced rather than on the value of the product. This led to striking fluctuations in tax revenues owing to the instability of salmon production; and as the total pack declined with depletion of the resource, tax revenues also declined even though the total value of the product was still increasing.

Governor Gruening proposed to rectify these inequities through

[41] Rogers, *op. cit.*, p. 164.

[42] Message of the Governor of Alaska to the Territorial Legislature, 1941, as quoted in: *Pacific Fisherman*, March 1941, p. 21.

the passage of a general 4 per cent corporation tax to be assessed on all net income from sources in Alaska. He also proposed a net-income tax on individuals to be graduated from 2 to 5 per cent. These proposals were moderate by all standards of state taxation. Nevertheless, when the measures were introduced in the territorial legislature, the canned-salmon lobby succeeded in combining with other nonresident lobbyists to bring about their defeat. In each succeeding territorial legislature measures to accomplish these purposes were introduced and defeated in a similar fashion.

By 1949 the tide had turned in Alaska and the canned-salmon lobby could no longer think of the territorial legislature as a mere "toy for Alaskans to play politics with" which could be easily manipulated. In speaking of the tides of change sweeping the Alaskan fisheries as operations opened for 1949, the editor of the industry trade journal said:

> The Alaska legislature was a smooth working coalition steamroller with Governor Gruening at the controls. It operated on a frank program of increased appropriations for education, health and social services, with the bill charged to the fisheries.[43]

The 1949 Legislature completely overhauled the territory's obsolete and inadequate tax system. A net-income tax and a property tax were enacted for the first time. A raw-fish tax based on the wholesale value of the canned-salmon pack replaced the old per case tax. License fees for resident and nonresident fishermen were increased. Fish trap license fees were increased and a graduated tax on fish caught by traps was provided. This latter tax was immediately attacked in the federal courts by the canners on the basis that it was enacted not to obtain revenue but to penalize the trap in relation to all other gear and hence was an infringement of the right to fish provided by the White Act. The tax was subsequently rejected as illegal in the District Court.[44] Other aspects of the new revenue measures were challenged in the courts, but with minor exceptions were upheld.[45] As a result of these fiscal

---

[43] *Pacific Fisherman*, May 1949, p. 25. (It was noted with disdain that Governor Gruening had been reappointed "assuring the salmon industry of an ardent opponent" for the next four years.)

[44] P. E. Harris & Co. *v.* Mullaney, *et al.*, 12 Alaska 476 and 87 F. Supp. 248.

[45] The nonresident fisherman license of $50 was declared excessive in comparison to the resident fee of $5. Anderson *v.* Mullaney, 13 Alaska 574, 191 F. 2d 123.

reforms the territory at last was able to improve its programs of health, education, welfare, and policing, and take on important new functions which had been neglected in the past owing to the limitation of funds.

Another forward step by the 1949 Legislature was the creation of a territorial Department of Fisheries which reflected the concern of Alaskans with the failure of the federal bureaucracy to conserve the salmon fisheries. It was the legislature's intent that the new department "take appropriate steps to improve Alaska's fisheries" and prepare for the assumption of complete management in the event of statehood or earlier transfer of control from the Department of the Interior.[46] While the new department had no power in the field of regulation owing to the prohibitions of the Organic Act, it was able to assist and supplement the work of the Fish and Wildlife Service in the fields of scientific research, stream improvement, and law enforcement.[47]

These and other actions taken by the territory in the following years—such as the referendum in 1952[48] in which the people of Alaska asked Congress by a vote of 20,544 to 3,479 to transfer control of the fisheries to the territory—were clear indications that new and strongly organized forces had gained control in Alaska. The extent of the packers' concern over these developments was revealed by the ferocity of the attack made upon Governor Gruening in the industry trade journal shortly after the 1952 general elections in which the Republican victories on the national level were duplicated in Alaska with the election of a predominantly Republican legislature. The editor spoke of the destructive course pursued by Gruening in which past legislatures had "blindly followed malign policies dictated by a governor intent upon entrenching his own far-to-the-left political position."[49] In the following month the journal continued its attack and it was noted that "most thoughtful men in

---

[46] *Session Laws of Alaska*, 1949, Chap. 68.

[47] The Alaska legislature in 1919 created a Territorial Fish Commission which devoted its efforts chiefly to fish culture, the removal of natural barriers in salmon streams, and the destruction of predatory enemies of salmon. At its biennial session in 1927, the legislature abolished the commission. Establishment of the Alaska Department of Fisheries revived many of the functions of its predecessor agency.

[48] *Session Laws of Alaska*, 1951, Chap. 89.

[49] *Pacific Fisherman*, November 1952, p. 1.

the industry" believed the effects of the elections on both the national and the territorial levels would be favorable to the industry. The editorial concluded that "come spring . . . the Governor of Alaska will be gone, leaving Alaska free once more to work out its future on the basis of free enterprise unfettered by paternalistic pandering."[50] But the ills of the salmon industry were much too basic to be influenced materially by a change of political party, and depletion of the resource continued its inexorable course.

In another editorial in the trade journal in 1952 the editor attempted to capture the suspense and drama in the industry at this juncture, and in so doing he unwittingly created a revealing picture of the packers bent on making their profits in spite of the critical condition of the resource. Said the editor:

> All the elements of a suspense drama were blended in the Alaska salmon season preliminaries this spring. There was a *race*—against time, against sturdy competitors. There was a *motive*—money running into millions. There was *love-interest*—developing in uncounted herds of salmon. There was *conflict*—of men jockeying and wrestling for position and advantage. . . . There was a *game*—experts playing poker, trying to wait each other out until one should weaken—playing for gigantic stakes in profit or loss; in big shares or none; in pay-checks or "rocking chair money." And all the while time was ticking out, as out in the North Pacific somewhere Nature was ripening the Reds, marshaling them by millions—for this is the Big Year—and pointing them toward Bristol Bay where they would run in the fullness of their time whether the Men were ready or not.[51]

But his composition considered only the superficial aspects of the drama that was being enacted. Nothing was said about the natural resource that was being unmercifully destroyed by these actions. Nothing was said about the fishermen and the people of Alaska who

[50] *Ibid.*, December 1952, p. 11. (The editorial concluded with the following warning to the packers and the new policy makers: "It should be recognized that while the election will make wide changes in the levels where policies are made, it will make but few in the levels where policies are applied—for these levels are protected by civil service with its guaranteed tenure. Moreover, it is at these protracted levels that some of the most insidious elements have penetrated the Service. The queer thinkers will still be there after January 20. They will retreat back into the woodwork, true; but they will still be there, quietly boring. . . . The new policymakers must keep close watch lest their policies be perverted by the entrenched heirs of Ickes and Chapman and Hiss and Acheson.")

[51] *Ibid.*, June 1952, p. 19.

were the real victims of the tragedy as one of their primary means of livelihood toppled toward ruin.

In 1953 the total Alaska canned-salmon pack amounted to less than three million cases, the lowest in forty-two years with the single exception of the 1921 failure. Economic distress among the fishermen and cannery workers in Alaska was so acute in the fall of that year that President Eisenhower, at the appeal of territorial authorities, declared parts of Alaska to be "disaster areas" and federal relief funds and food supplies from the Department of Agriculture surplus were sent there. Public works projects and other stopgap measures were immediately instigated with both federal and territorial funds in an attempt to lessen the impact of the fishery failure.[52] As the former Territorial Governor Ernest Gruening pointed out in his history of Alaska[53] published in the following year:

> Designation of a "disaster area" by the federal government customarily followed major calamities such as flood, drought, hurricane, tornado, earthquake, conflagration or pestilence, usually referred to as an "act of God." It was unique and unprecedented in the failure of a federally managed resource, attributable, rather, to the acts of man. But there was little question of the gravity of the disaster and of the need for help.[54]

In neighboring British Columbia, divided from Alaska only by an imaginary political line, the salmon fishery was in a healthy and productive condition. The contrast between the two regions was a sharp one. In southeast Alaska, for example, the average pack of pink salmon during the past eight years had been but 63 per cent of the forty-year average, while during the same period the average British Columbia pink pack had been 101.2 per cent of the forty-year average.

In spite of the accelerated downward trend in total catch, the Service was reluctant to admit publicly that the conservation program was failing. As late as 1949, for example, the chief of the Alaska Fisheries Branch analyzed the situation in the following terms:

---

[52] U.S. Department of the Interior, *Report of the Governor of Alaska to the Secretary* (Washington: U.S. Government Printing Office, 1954), pp. 2-3.

[53] Gruening, *op. cit.*, p. 405.

[54] Gruening, *op. cit.*, p. 405.

> Total salmon production has been below normal in Alaska for the last six years because of the reduced abundance in one or more areas, *primarily from natural causes.* A disproportionately large part of these runs was reserved for spawning purposes to provide runs of normal volume in the next cycle. There is every reason to be optimistic that this watchful management will maintain this resource at its most productive level.[55]

But by 1953 it had become obvious to everyone connected with the fishery that a crisis existed.

In 1954 the Fish and Wildlife Service belatedly initiated a vigorous program to rehabilitate the resource. Congress seemed to recognize the seriousness of the situation and funds more commensurable with the needs began to be made available to the federal agency. Scientific research was increased and stringent emergency regulations aimed at greatly reducing fishing pressures on the resource were put into effect. These efforts were unable to halt the downward trend in the total pack. Attempts were made to have the White Act revised and to gain authority to control the amount of gear in the fishery, but, as in the past, these failed. An area-licensing system was conceived as an alternative means of reducing fishing pressures within the purview of the White Act, but objection to even this lesser degree of control was so great that the Service was unable to put it fully into effect until the 1956 season. Under this system, men and gear were licensed to fish in a specific area and were prevented from moving from area to area to catch the peak of the runs. This helped to reduce the massing and concentration of gear after the season began, but it had no effect whatever on the over-all amount of gear in the fishery.

While the prices of all species of canned salmon had wavered slightly in the early 1950s, giving rise to a slight panic in the industry, by 1954 the continuous upward trend resumed and in 1957 the industry trade journal was able to report that the old cry of "salmon is priced out of the market" was no longer heard even though prices were higher than ever.[56] Major contributing factors to the improved marketing picture were the removal by Great Britain of import restrictions on the purchase of canned

[55] Seton H. Thompson, "Management of the Marine Resources of Alaska," *Science in Alaska* (Washington: Arctic Institute of North America, 1952) pp. 285-286.

[56] *Pacific Fisherman,* January 1957 (Yearbook), p. 158.

salmon which had been in effect since World War II and the high and rising national economy and population reflecting consumer buying power at a record level. As in the past, rising prices continued to induce more gear into the fishery. Each individual packer and fisherman strained every muscle to increase his share of the diminishing supply while at the same time hoping that nothing would happen to adversely influence the price he would receive.

It was indeed a boom-or-bust situation in which some made big money while others were left destitute, depending upon whether the fish materialized in the particular area one was operating that year. Disregard of the law became commonplace, and those who succeeded in making an illegal haul were all too often looked upon with envy by their fellow fishermen. The Fish and Wildlife Service instituted a much more rigorous enforcement program. New boats and airplanes were added to increase the efficiency of the force, and hundreds of stream guards were employed each year to patrol the mouths of streams; but the incentive for violation was so high that no economically feasible program of enforcement could adequately cope with the problem.

Then in the mid-fifties another conflict arose. It added a new and unknown dimension to the problems of rehabilitating the resource and greatly confused an already chaotic state of affairs. It was the problem of foreign competition by the Japanese in the harvesting of the resource. While statehood, trap elimination, federal *versus* territorial control, and other issues of a like nature continued to divide and fracture the industry into a number of highly antagonistic groups, this new international complication drew all the splintered forces together, united against what was considered a common threat. A detailed evaluation of this urgent issue is beyond the scope of this study and only a brief sketch of some of the important ramifications can be presented here.

Since the early 1900s the Japanese had fished for salmon along the Asian coast. In the early 1930s Japan began high-seas fishing for salmon off the Siberian coast, and later in the decade experimental and survey vessels were sent to explore the international waters off Bristol Bay. Some salmon were taken at that time. The United States government protested and Japan withdrew. The event created a genuine scare among American fishermen and industrial interests, and following World War II measures were taken by the

United States to prevent Japan from fishing salmon which spawned in American streams. Subsequently, Japan was forced by the Peace Treaty to join Canada and the United States as a party to the International North Pacific Fisheries Convention, which was eventually signed and ratified by all three nations in 1954.[57]

To prevent the Japanese from catching American-spawned salmon on the high seas a provisional line was drawn far out in the Pacific Ocean (at 175° west longitude) which, it was thought, satisfactorily divided American- from Asian-spawned salmon. Japan was to abstain from fishing for salmon beyond that line as long as Canada and the United States continued to fully utilize and regulate that fishery. American interests were confident that the "abstention line," unprecedented under international law, would forever assure the exclusion of Japanese from catching American-spawned salmon.[58]

Following the ratification of the convention Japan, keeping at all times within the terms of the treaty, began a large-scale high-seas salmon operation employing newly developed gear and techniques, and the total catch began to increase phenomenally. In 1952 the Japanese high-seas salmon catch amounted to only 2.1 million fish. The catch jumped to 7.7 million fish in 1953, to 20.5 million in 1954, and to over 60 million fish by 1957. As the Japanese catch increased and the Alaska catch continued its downward trend, the American interests began to see a grim relationship between the two phenomena even though there was no scientific basis upon which to substantiate this circumstantial evidence. For example, at hearings held by a Senate committee in Alaska and Seattle in 1955 to investigate problems of fisheries management, of all factors which might possibly have contributed to the downward spiral of salmon harvests, none was mentioned more frequently than that of Japanese encroachment.[59] The clamor increased and in a short time Japan had become the primary scapegoat for nearly all the ills besetting the Alaska salmon fishery.

---

[57] Made effective by an Act of August 12, 1954, 68 Stat. 698.

[58] Crudely stated, the principle of abstention is based on a belief that if a stock of fish has been exploited historically by one or more nations that have made sacrifices to conserve it, other nations should stay out of this fishery.

[59] Reported in: U.S. Senate, *Pacific Coast and Alaska Fisheries*, Report of the Committee on Interstate and Foreign Commerce pursuant to S.R. 13 and S.R. 163, 84C:2s, (Washington: Government Printing Office, 1956), p. 4.

Two new organizations encompassing all interest groups within the industry were formed to press actively for the protection of the salmon resources of North America.[60] Unsuccessful attempts were made to get legislation through Congress that would bring pressure to bear on Japanese fishing activities through various economic sanctions such as the banning of imports from Japan of canned salmon and other fishery products. An attempt was also made to get organized labor to refuse to unload goods from Japan at the port of entry in the United States unless Japan agreed to certain stipulations in connection with their high-seas salmon fishing.

In the meantime scientific investigations by the American section of the International North Pacific Fisheries Commission were greatly stepped up. By the late 1950s enough scientific evidence was available to show that Asian- and American-spawned salmon intermingled over a broad zone in the middle of the Pacific Ocean, and that some American-spawned salmon, especially the reds of Bristol Bay, did in fact travel westward beyond the abstention line during their ocean migrations. On the basis of this evidence the American section began pressing at the annual meetings of the Commission for a movement of the abstention line farther westward toward Japan. The Japanese, on the basis of their own scientific studies, maintained that there was a great variation in the size and movement of stocks of these salmon from one year to another and that much more conclusive evidence of a quantitative and qualitative nature would be necessary before there could be any serious discussion of the need to move the existing abstention line. The two countries are presently at a deadlock and negotiations are moving ahead slowly as the scientists of both countries feverishly seek scientific evidence to corroborate and substantiate the respective points of view.

Canadian scientists have apparently come to the conclusion that few if any Canadian-spawned salmon are being caught by the Japanese on the high seas under the existing terms of the Treaty. Their primary concern is that the Japanese continue to refrain from fishing salmon eastward of the existing abstention line. The terms of the Treaty will be subject to revision in June 1963, and the Canadians fear that if the Japanese are pressed too hard they might

[60] For a full description of these organizations and their composition see: *Pacific Fisherman*, January 1958, p. 9.

refuse to recognize the principle of abstention altogether.[61] If this should occur, the Japanese would be legally free to fish for salmon just outside the three-mile limit along the North American coastline. The Canadian viewpoint was summed up in an editorial in the *Canadian Western Fisherman* in 1957:

> Time is an unalterable factor in research. You can't rush scientists. . . . Fishermen . . . will have to be patient. Throwing the problem into the political arena, as the American Salmon Industry has done, will not speed research. It is more likely to stir up storms of verbosity, which may conceivably rain only suspicion and hatred.[62]

The problems raised by this international situation are so numerous and complicated as to be almost imponderable. There is very little hope for the future survival of the resource unless adequate means can be found to control *all* fishing intensity in an equitable manner, no matter what the nationality of the fishermen may be. This, with all its ramifications, is undoubtedly the central issue facing the International Commission. Obviously Alaska and the United States will have no lasting interest in maintaining expensive salmon-conservation programs to support high-seas salmon harvests by the fishermen of other nations.

While it is too early to determine the eventual outcome, in looking at the issue within the context of this study there are certain important aspects which must be noted. First, as the problem of conserving the Alaska salmon moves to the international level, the absurdity of defining conservation only in biological terms of maximum sustained yield immediately becomes apparent. It was the Fish and Wildlife Service policy, it may be recalled, that the federal agency was interested only in maintaining the stock of fish and not in the social and economic aspects of who caught the fish. The international conflict serves to illustrate how meaningless is a management approach that does not consider who catches the fish. Second, in the excitement of the international conflict, Japan frequently has been blamed for the failure of the salmon resource throughout Alaska. However, the downward trend in salmon harvests began almost two decades before the Japanese started fishing on the high

---

[61] The Treaty runs for a minimum of ten years from June 1953 and will continue thereafter until one year after notice of intention to terminate is given by one of the parties to the Convention.

[62] *Canadian Western Fisheries,* Vol. 55, No. 2, November 1957, p. 7.

seas. Scientific research by the American section indicates that the Japanese high-seas salmon fishery has had little adverse impact on American catches except with respect to the important red salmon runs into Bristol Bay, and even here the relationship is not fully known. It is not only a distortion of the facts to blame the Japanese for the present widespread depleted condition of the Alaska salmon runs, but the existence of this convenient scapegoat has tended to distract from conservation issues on the domestic level. Even if equitable means are found to prevent the Japanese from catching American-spawned salmon on the high seas, the danger of complete destruction of the resource still exists.

PART THREE

SEQUENCE AND CONSEQUENCE

8 *Analysis and Critique*

THIS IS THE PATHETIC history of the ruinous exploitation of one of the nation's important renewable natural resources, a food source requiring no capital outlay or labor to sow and cultivate and one which can be harvested extremely economically if managed properly. What happened? Why is the resource in the state it is today? One need only thumb through one of the many volumes of congressional hearings to find that there are almost as many different answers as there are participants. In most cases the tendency has been to find a single whipping boy. Some blame the rapaciousness of the canners—the Fish Trust, the absentee capitalists, the traps. Others blame the fishermen for their greed—their readiness to violate the law, the creek robbers. Some blame predators and other natural causes. Some lay the blame on the Japanese. Others place the blame on maladministration—weak regulations, lack of appropriations, inadequate enforcement. Everyone has his own pet theory and is willing to voice it.

In most cases each also has had a simple cure, a panacea that, if adopted, would right all the wrongs, correct all the evils, and lead the fishery back to a healthy state. Outlaw the traps. Kill all the eagles, beluga whales, gulls, dolly varden trout, seals. Give the territory control of the fisheries. Statehood. Artificial propagation.

Force the Japanese to stop fishing "our" salmon. Break the monopoly. Prevent overescapement. Provide stringent enforcement. Fish-farming. More scientific knowledge. Take fisheries out of "politics." And so on *ad infinitum.* It would be wonderful if there were one problem, one culprit, and one simple solution. But these isolated examples are only symptoms of much more basic and complex problems, and unless these are fully recognized and acted upon there is little hope that the resource can survive many more years of exploitation. This study has shown that the level of production and hence the pattern and extent of exploitation has been the result of the action and interaction of many different forces and pressures—biological, economic, political, and social. This concluding chapter examines these four broad areas and their relation to each other in an effort to show in their true perspective the basic problems of conserving the resource.

First there is the biological environment. The size of the salmon population is determined by numerous biological and ecological influences, many of which are not subject to manipulation or control by man. Water temperatures, climatic variations, predation, food supply, and many other natural factors have already been discussed. The condition of this complex biological environment is one of the most important elements in determining the supply of the resource and its reproductive abilities. The size of the salmon population available in any given year is also directly related to the extent to which the stocks of fish were exploited by man in preceding years. As was pointed out, there is a close relationship in the salmon fishery between the catch, the escapement, and the number of fish available to the fishery a few years hence. This is the fascinating and highly complex domain of the fisheries biologist—population dynamics, growth rates, natural mortality, and effort–yield relationships. The biologist cannot observe the resource directly, as in the case of forestry, nor can he run controlled experiments. Most of his data come from nonrandom observations provided by the commercial fishery. The biological side of fishery management calls not only for patient, expensive research, but for wise judgment based on intimate experience in the interpretation of partial information. The biologist has an extremely important but unenviable function to perform.[1] Because of his training and particular interest in the re-

[1] Crutchfield, *op. cit.*, p. 3.

U.S. Fish & Wildlife Service

A fish ladder on Fall Creek near Petersburg, Alaska, allows salmon to by-pass an otherwise insurmountable series of waterfalls.

source, the biologist has seen the problem of conservation primarily in physical terms, and the objective of management is most always stated in terms of maximum sustained yield.

The biological environment is a major constraint on man's behavior, for the environment is finite and capable of being effectively exploited only up to a point. It sets a limit on what man can do. Scientific knowledge of the resource and this biological environment is of utmost importance in the conduct of a sound management program. Unfortunately that knowledge has been sadly deficient in the Alaska salmon fishery, and this deficiency has provided a fertile field for personal opinion and speculation. There is great need for fuller scientific knowledge.

Second, there is the economic sphere within which the resource has been exploited. There is no purpose in managing the resource except that it has value to man, and because we are talking about a commercial fishery in a competitive economy, that value can be measured directly in terms of dollars.[2] The marketing outlook determines the intensity of fishing and processing efforts at any given time. In the broad sense that the term is used here, marketing outlook depends upon various factors including the costs of production, the probable prices consumers will be willing to pay for the finished product as well as the prices and quantities of competing foods, the availability of credit, and other economic factors. Each individual operator or fisherman weighs the facts available to him and plans his course of action for the season accordingly. The sum of all these individual decisions determines the over-all extent of operations for that year.

Dr. Crutchfield has stated the economist's viewpoint in the following terms:

> It is simply impossible to make sense of conservation except in economic terms. Why conserve salmon at all? Unless the end-products of the fishery are worth more than the cost of producing them there would be neither a fishery nor a conservation problem. Physical yield becomes important only if the value of the fish is assumed. The clarity of maximum physical yield as an objective becomes even more dubious if we regard the fisheries of Alaska as a whole, rather than singly. If part of the capital and labor now used in the salmon fishery were diverted to catch-

---

[2] There are other values of salmon to man, such as its recreation value, which are not considered here. However, the statements would also apply to these values.

ing cod and dogfish it is possible that we could expand *physical* output considerably. Obviously this would be nonsense—but only because the value of the catch, to consumers and producers, would be reduced.[3]

The economics of salmon conservation is greatly complicated by the institution of a free and common fishery. As was shown in Chapter 1, the common-property aspect means that conservation in terms of voluntary restraint can never be a practical economic objective for the individual. Commissioner O'Malley recognized this in 1920 when he concluded that whatever the individual spared for spawning purposes his competitors would thankfully accept and place in cans. The individual, he said, is powerless to conserve either in the public interest or in his own private interest by listening to counsels of moderation (see pp. 107 ff.). This study has shown that with free entry of men and gear into the fishery, the level of fishing effort tended toward the maximum the fishery could sustain rather than toward the minimum amount, which would prevail in the case of a privately-owned resource. This led to a consistent overcapacity in fishing gear and men. As the supply began to decrease from overfishing, the fishing effort continued to rise at a rapid rate in response to rising demand and price. More and more men were catching fewer and fewer fish. By the late 1950s there were four times more fishermen than in the early 1900s and each was catching less than one-third the number of fish. The net value of the fishery was simply dissipated in excessive costs. Thus, it was concluded that the level of fishing effort and hence the extent of overfishing depended as much on economic factors influencing costs and prices as on the biological factors affecting yield.

Third, there is the political arena within which the direction and scope of the government conservation program was determined. The political process has been characterized by bitter and prolonged conflict among the interest groups and between these groups and the regulating agency. These conflicts and the resulting policies that were formulated cannot be fully understood except in light of the economic forces mentioned above. The participants were faced with a set of economic conditions which greatly limited their choice of action. Under a common-property arrangement and the competitive conditions that prevail, conservation by admonition is useless.

---

[3] Crutchfield, *op. cit.* p. 6.

It is foolish to expect either industry or labor to voluntarily accept a course of action which only leads them to economic disaster in the hope that if each moves toward disaster all will be saved. The only real choice the participants had was to stay in or get out of the fishery. If they chose the former, it was necessary for them to take actions and adopt practices that would allow them to survive in the competitive battle; if they chose the latter, others eagerly took their place in the fishery. This by no means absolves the participants of their actions but it does help us to understand why the political process was fraught with conflict and controversy. It also explains why conservation of the Alaska salmon resource is not simply a problem of educating the participants. Each tends to rationalize his own actions and to find a scapegoat for the outcome of the actions of all. The result is a fantasy in which the truth becomes lost in a sea of meaningless jargon. Everyone is for restriction —on the other fellow.

The federal regulatory agency never succeeded in gaining authority to control the amount of gear in the fishery. Instead policies were adopted that were aimed at decreasing the efficiency of men and gear. As already mentioned, this led to overcapitalization and serious economic waste. In terms of the political arena, it also led to an intensification of conflict among the groups as each sought through the political process to shift the burden of conservation to others. It greatly accentuated the enforcement problem and made the salmon industry more vulnerable to the increasingly serious competition from imports and foreign encroachment.

The federal agency never developed and carried out a consistent, clear-cut policy with respect to efficiency. In its promotional role the federal agency fostered technological advances in boats and gear and provided various programs of aid to the fishermen with a view to increasing their returns from the fishery, while in its regulatory role the agency promulgated regulations designed to counter technological advance in an effort to reduce fishing pressures. Another example was the varying degrees in which the policy of reducing efficiency was applied to the several types of gear. Until as late as 1951 the federal agency prohibited fishing in Bristol Bay except by the grossly inefficient sailboat, yet on the other hand the agency defended the continued use of the highly efficient trap in other fishing districts. As long as there was a significant disparity in the basic productivity of the various types of gear, a policy of reducing efficiency was extremely difficult to apply in an equitable manner and nearly every decision was vulnerable to charges of favoritism, collusion, and political intrigue. It was not conducive to respect for the agency and the regulations that were promulgated to control fishing.

This confusion of promotional and regulatory roles had other policy implications. As was pointed out in the study, through its promotional role the federal agency was drawn into close personal relationships with the fishery interests it was supposed to be regulating, and the atmosphere was not conducive to the formulation and execution of a rigorous, objective and impartial regulatory program. Instead it led to a search for some way to conserve without restricting. The result was a misguided emphasis on artificial propagation and an exaggerated accentuation of predation and other natural factors as causes of depletion.

Another significant political factor which strongly influenced policy decisions grew out of the circumstance that federal management of commercial fisheries was unique to Alaska. Elsewhere this was the primary responsibility of the state or territorial government, with the federal government merely providing supplementary research, guidance, and promotion. As was pointed out in the introduction, during the early years many persons believed that the federal government, with its superior financial resources and its broader view of the public interest, would be in a much stronger position to withstand political pressures and take the necessary coercive actions, and, hence, would be able to develop and execute a rational conservation program that could be held up to the individual states as a model of how complex fishery-management problems should be handled.

This study has shown that, on the contrary, the political process did not function properly under this unique structure. In the first place the federal commercial-fisheries program led a roving life amongst federal bureaus, and this in itself was not conducive to the development and execution of a rational fishery-conservation program for Alaska. In the second place, as mentioned above, the primary function of the regulating agency for many years was to promote, foster, and develop the industry, and the resulting confusion of its roles led to an unduly close relationship with the industry. In the third place, federal control led to a political imbalance among the pressure groups which greatly favored the absentee interests in the process of policy formation. The canners, for example, had direct access to Congress through their senators and representatives from the West coast, while another basic segment of the industry—the resident fishermen and other territorial interests—had only the voice of a voteless delegate. This provided the absentee canners with extraordinary leverage in Congress where the majority of the members were generally unconcerned and uninformed about purely local matters in the territory of Alaska. These same congressmen could also be called upon by their constituents—the nonresident canners and labor groups—for assistance in dealing with administration officials on important matters concerning conservation of the Alaska salmon.

This political imbalance was accentuated by the centralization at the Washington level of nearly all administrative decisions relating to the Alaska fisheries. Invariably only the views of those capable of traveling to the Nation's capital were heard by the congressmen and administrative officials. The federal administrators at times so fully accepted the views of the packers that they frequently acted as spokesmen and chief lobbyists for this segment of their clientele. What emerged was not vigorous, impartial federal management of the Alaska resource, but joint management shared with an absentee industry. The result was a conservation program strongly oriented toward interests outside Alaska.

If a criterion of democracy is the widest possible participation in governmental decision-making, the political process here described left much to be desired. Political and economic strength was centered in the hands of a few absentee corporate presidents and managers who themselves had little firsthand knowledge of the condition of the resource, and who were interested primarily if not exclusively in maintaining profits and dividends from their investments in the remote northern region of Alaska. It is only within this political context that one can begin to understand why Congress and the federal agency for many years were complacent about the condition of the Alaska salmon resource, and why the government seemed unable to act in accordance with the needs except at times of crisis when conservation in terms of reduced output was to the economic advantage of the stronger interests.

It also helps to explain the inability of the federal agency to obtain adequate appropriations for the conduct of the program, for enforcement and for scientific study, and why the industry was so strongly opposed to territorial control of the fishery and to statehood. Because the wealthy and politically potent salmon canners chose to use their great powers in a negative and obstructionist manner in an attempt to maintain the status quo, they must be charged with a larger part of the responsibility for the results.

The fourth and final area to be considered here is the social sphere which, though more nebulous and difficult to define than the other three, is nonetheless of prime importance, for it is here that the essence of conservation lies. The federal agency insisted upon defining the goal of management in purely physical terms of maximum sustained yield, and it successfully resisted every effort to broaden this goal to encompass the human element. This was primarily the result of two influences. First, biologists have held a dominant position not only in scientific research, but also in the top administrative echelon of the federal agency handling the Alaska salmon conservation program. Their education and training led them to see the task of conservation primarily if not solely in its physical dimensions, and in setting policy they chose to regard the salmon fishery as if it were a noncommercial wildlife resource. Second, this narrow interpretation of the meaning of conservation was strongly favored by the politically potent canned-salmon lobby which feared that any widening of the concept to include consideration of broad social ends would result in a change in the status quo contrary to their interests.

Thus, while the agency overtly claimed to be dedicated solely to pure biology and the preservation of fish, in pursuing this asocial policy it was unwittingly promoting certain antisocial ends of the absentee packers. It was to the economic advantage of the packers, for example, that the federal agency refused to consider the impact of its conservation regulations on the economic and social well-being of the people of Alaska; on the development of permanent well-rounded settlement; on the stability of the society that was emerging; on the pattern of employment and the resident–nonresident conflict; on the cultural transition of the aboriginal populations; and on the natural political aspirations of the people. Gifford Pinchot posed the issue succinctly as early as 1911 in the following terms:

Two solutions of the Alaska question are possible today. We can let Alaska become the private preserve of a few great special interests to be developed and controlled at their pleasure and as their profit may dictate. . . . Or we can treat Alaska as the future home of hundreds of thousands of free American citizens, and its resources as a trust to be developed and conserved for their benefit and for the benefit of all the people—who are its owners.[4]

In not recognizing the social implications of the task, the federal agency bred widespread resentment, mistrust, and disregard of the laws. Trap piracy, attempted bribery of officials, creek-robbing and other wanton violations of the regulations became commonplace, and those who succeeded in making an illegal haul or who outwitted the government in other ways were regarded with approbation and envy by their fellow man. In short, a social environment was created which compounded the difficulties of management and enforcement and added fuel to an already inflamed political milieu.

The state of Alaska faces a tremendous task as it attempts to rehabilitate the salmon resource to something of its former grandeur. The lack of adequate biological knowledge and the need for much more study and research has already been stressed. The state must be willing and able to invest heavily in a large-scale program of research and management with little likelihood of a significant return on the investment for many years to come. While the willingness may be there, the ability to finance it remains a crucial question, for the state must meet many new financial obligations that are concomitant with statehood. In light of the condition of the legacy handed the state, it would seem that the federal government has an especially deep obligation to provide the greatest possible assistance in this endeavor. As Senator Gruening pointed out in a recent speech on the floor of the United States Senate:

Had it not been for the Federal Government's neglecting and permitting the abuse of the salmon fisheries resource of Alaska, they would today constitute a great and rich heritage for this and future generations. . . .

The record is there. It is, therefore, fitting and proper that the trustee who failed the trust—the Federal Government—should now do its part to make whole the trust—to rehabilitate the Alaska fishing resources.[5]

---

[4] *Saturday Evening Post,* December 16, 1911, pp. 12 ff.

[5] U.S. *Congressional Record,* June 10, 1960 (reprint), 4 pp.

But it is important to realize that research alone is no panacea. Many management decisions must be made that necessarily will have an adverse impact on almost every segment of the industry, for the resource cannot be rebuilt for the future without reducing the demands upon it today. The state administration is presently enjoying a brief period of relative political calm as the interest groups reorganize and begin to build new lines of communications and access to the crucial points of decision-making under the new political jurisdiction. The political pressures will surely mount with the severity of the decisions, and the success of the rehabilitation program will depend upon the ability of the state to withstand these pressures, both internal and external.

Furthermore, there is no reason whatever to expect that the state government can succeed where the federal government failed unless the state is willing to embark upon a long-range program based on a complete reformulation of the conservation problem in terms of economic, political, social, and biological reality. This is the area of critical importance, for there is indication that the state merely intends to adopt the old, narrow approach of the federal agency without realizing that seeds of failure lie in the approach. Indeed, if this approach is accepted as a constant which cannot be changed, the federal agency deserves praise rather than criticism, for making the supply stretch as far as it has. It must be recognized, as it has been in other renewable natural-resource management fields, that it is simply not enough to say that the ultimate ends should be the perpetuation of the resource on a sustained-yield basis. It must be recognized that the welfare of people and not fish is the *raison d'être* for a management program, and that if maximum sustained yield has any validity, it is as a means to important human ends rather than as an end in itself. It must be recognized that the biological requirements of the resource can be met through various alternative means, that the social and economic costs and benefits of these alternatives vary greatly, and that it is impossible to make a rational choice of means unless the ultimate goals to be accomplished are stated in human terms.

There is need to study the ultimate ends the state wishes to promote through the use of the natural-resource base. There is need to explore the repercussions of various measures of public control and economic regulations and thus to provide at least tentative criteria for the formulation of public policy beyond that of the inadequate maximum sustained-yield concept, and thereby enable government officials to make reasoned choices in full understanding of the probable results of their actions. There is need to recognize that the ancient concept of a free and common fishery places serious institutional restraints on decision-making which stand in the way of rational behavior of fishermen and processors, and prevent the government from conducting a sane conservation program. There is need to recognize that unless this major obstacle is overcome the industry will decline steadily as a source of revenue to the state and as a source of income to its residents. There is need to recognize that this is a man-made social institution which can be modified by man, and that the amount of gear in the fishery can be controlled without doing violence to the democratic process and American concepts of law and equity. There is need for action before the opportunity is lost.

Appendix A. Statistical Sources

THE THREE MAJOR SOURCES for historical statistics on the Alaska salmon fishery are: (1) *Alaska Fishery and Fur-Seal Industries,* which has been published annually since 1905 by the Bureau of Fisheries and the Fish and Wildlife Service respectively; (2) *Alaska Fisheries,* an annual statistical summary published by the same agencies since 1927; and (3) the annual yearbooks of the *Pacific Fisherman,* which contain statistical data compiled by the industry as well as summaries of some of the series compiled by the federal government. The yearbooks have been published every year since 1902. Statistical data are fairly complete and standardized since 1905, when the Bureau of Fisheries was established. For earlier statistics, one must look to the annual reports of the Treasury agents and the United States Fish Commission.

The sources used for each of the figures in this study are given below. Most of the data were plotted on a semilogarithmic scale to facilitate comparison of proportional rates of change.

Figure 2. SOURCE: *Alaska Fishery and Fur-Seal Industries.* The publication lists each company by name and the number and location of canneries and traps operated. Data on the five companies operating the largest number of traps each year were compiled to show the extent of concentration of ownership. Five-year averages were used to show the general trend.

Figure 3. SOURCE: Data for the years 1878 to 1904 were taken from *Pacific Fisherman* (Yearbook), January 1930, p. 90, and for the years from 1905 to 1958 from *Pacific Fisherman* (Yearbook), January 1960, p. 73.

Figure 4. SOURCE: *Pacific Fisherman* (Yearbook), January 1960, pp. 55, 57.

Figure 5. SOURCE: *Ibid.*, pp. 57, 77, 80, 89.

Figure 6. SOURCE: *Ibid.*, p. 73.

Figure 7. SOURCE: Same as Figure 3.

Figure 9. SOURCE: *Alaska Fishery and Fur-Seal Industries* for data up to 1955, and *Alaska Fisheries* for data from 1956 to 1959.

Figure 10. SOURCE: Same as Figure 9. Averages were calculated from these data by dividing the annual total catch for each type of gear by the total number of units that were operating. Five-year moving averages were calculated to show the secular trend.

Figure 11. SOURCE: Same as Figure 9.

Figure 12. SOURCE: Same as Figure 9. The "cannery and all other" category includes shoremen, transporters, and all other nonfishing employees in the industry.

Figure 13. SOURCE: Same as Figure 9. The average catch per fisherman was calculated by subtracting the trap-caught fish from the total catch and dividing by the number of fishermen.

Figure 14. SOURCE: Same as Figure 9. The average annual prices per case of canned salmon was divided by the Wholesale Price Index of the Bureau of Labor Statistics (1947-1949 = 100) to obtain a real price. Source for the price index is: U.S. Department of Commerce, *Historical Statistics of the United States, Colonial Times to 1957* (Washington: U.S. Government Printing Office, 1960), p. 117.

Figure 15. SOURCE: *Pacific Fisherman* (Yearbook), January 1960, p. 57. Five-year averages were calculated and freehand curves were drawn to indicate the secular trend.

Figure 16. SOURCE: James A. Crutchfield, "The Economics of Salmon Management" (unpublished paper delivered at the Alaska Science Conference, Juneau, Alaska, August 1959), p. 4.

Figure 17. SOURCE: Same as Figure 14. The average real price paid to the fishermen per fish was calculated in the following manner. The value of the trap-caught fish was subtracted from the total value of the catch to obtain the value of the catch to the fishermen. These values were corrected with the Wholesale Price Index (1947-1949 = 100) and divided by the total number of fish caught to obtain a weighted average real price. The average weighted real price per case of canned salmon was obtained by dividing the total real value of canned salmon by the total number of cases produced. (*Note:* since there is no data available showing the actual value of trap-caught fish, it was necessary to estimate this by assuming that the value of the catch was reduced by the same proportion the trap catch bears to the total catch.)

Figure 18. SOURCE: Same as Figure 14. Also see the remarks above under Figure 17.

Figure 19. SOURCE: Same as Figure 14. The average value of the catch per fisherman was calculated by subtracting the value of trap-caught fish from the total value of the catch and dividing by the number of fishermen. This was then corrected with the Consumer Price Index (1947-1949 = 100) to obtain the average real value per fisherman in terms of purchasing power.

Figure 20. SOURCE: *Pacific Fisherman* (Yearbook). January 1959, p. 94. The average real value of output per operating cannery was calculated by dividing the total value of production by the number of operating canneries and correcting with the Wholesale Price Index (1947-1949 = 100).

Appendix B. Supplemental Tables

TABLE 1

LICENSES AND BUSINESS TAXES PAID TO THE TERRITORY OF ALASKA BY THE COMMERCIAL FISHING INDUSTRY 1926-1958

Calendar Year	Amount	Per cent of Total Value of Canned Salmon	Per cent of Territorial Revenue
1958	$2,069,286	3.2	8.5
1957	2,462,966	2.5	10.5
1956	2,462,205	3.1	11.6
1955	2,278,465	3.9	13.4
1954	2,198,358	3.3	14.2
1953	2,642,883	2.3	16.0
1952	5,203,349	6.8	32.5
1951	2,741,606	3.5	19.8
1950	2,350,842	2.9	23.1
1949[a]	2,004,301	2.5	30.5
1948	719,260	0.7	14.1
1947	1,606,631	1.8	18.0
1946	887,124	1.5	27.1
1945	548,002	1.2	24.9
1944	767,170	1.5	32.1
1943	939,435	1.6	43.7
1942	443,323	0.9	18.6
1941	767,998	1.3	38.2
1940	509,297	1.6	26.2
1939	654,422	1.9	31.1
1938	900,894	2.5	46.4
1937	759,425	1.7	40.1
1936	507,966	1.1	44.7
1935	978,253	3.8	65.2
1934	923,511	2.5	77.1
1933	691,897	2.3	68.2
1932	664,110	3.2	78.2
1931	620,545	2.1	82.9
1930	519,003	1.7	[b]
1929	619,134	1.5	[b]
1928	734,904	1.6	[b]
1927	514,610	1.6	[b]
1926	814,390	1.8	[b]

SOURCE: *Annual Alaska Fishery and Fur-Seal Industries,* U.S. Fish and Wildlife Service.

[a] Territorial tax structure revised in 1949.

[b] Not available.

TABLE 2

FEDERAL FUNDS APPROPRIATED FOR CONSERVATION AND RESEARCH
ALASKA FISHERIES
1930-1959

Year	Management	Research	Total
1959	$1,510,025	$906,250	$2,416,275
1958	1,592,350	859,600	2,451,950
1957	1,390,590	952,750	2,343,340
1956	1,385,400	238,721	1,624,121
1955	1,265,600	175,000	1,440,600
1954	1,256,466	175,000	1,431,466
1953	1,099,718	172,000	1,271,718
1952	845,593	178,000	1,023,593
1951	873,884	178,700	1,052,584
1950	998,800[a]	150,000[b]	1,148,800
1949	712,400	197,900[b]	910,300
1948	472,400	105,300[b]	577,700
1947	442,957	59,500[b]	502,457
1946	297,046	56,000	353,046
1945	287,655	63,000	350,655
1944	259,020	63,000	322,020
1943	280,700	75,000	355,700
1942	247,060	84,200	331,260
1941	234,610	94,000	328,610
1940	213,510	103,000	316,510
1939	212,990	100,000	312,990
1938	205,810	32,000	237,810
1937	222,210	22,500	244,710
1936	213,720	18,500	232,220
1935	205,990	22,500	228,490
1934	208,300	22,500	230,800
1933	320,200	28,900	349,100
1932	392,600	31,200	423,800
1931	286,600	21,500	308,100
1930	261,963	12,400	274,363

SOURCE: Regional Office, U.S. Fish and Wildlife Service, Juneau, Alaska.

[a] Includes $250,000 for construction of aircraft facilities at Anchorage.
[b] Excludes stream improvement funds.

Bibliography

BOOKS

ANDREWS, C. L. *The Story of Alaska*. Caldwell: The Caxton Printers, 1938.

ANDREWS, RALPH W. *Fish and Ships*. Seattle: Superior Publishing Co., Inc., 1959.

BANCROFT, HUBERT HOWE. *History of Alaska, 1730-1885*. San Francisco: The History Co., 1886.

BINGHAM, JOSEPH W. *Report on the International Law of Pacific Coast Fisheries*. Stanford: Stanford University Press, 1939.

BRITISH COLUMBIA PROVINCIAL MUSEUM. *The Fresh-water Fishes of British Columbia*. Vancouver: Don McDiarmid Printers, 1959.

CARROTHERS, W. A. *The British Columbia Fisheries*. Toronto: University of Toronto, 1941.

CIRIACY-WANTRUP, S. V. *Resource Conservation—Economics and Policies*. Berkeley: University of California Press, 1952.

CLARK, H. W., *History of Alaska*. New York: Macmillan, 1930.

CURTIS, BRIAN. *The Life Story of the Fish*. New York: Harcourt, Brace and Co., 1949.

DELOACH, D. B. *Salmon Canning Industry*. Corvallis: Oregon State College, 1939.

DE LAGUNA, FREDERICA. *The Story of a Tlingit Community*. Smithsonian Institute Bulletin 172. Washington: U.S. Government Printing Office, 1960.

DRUCKER, PHILIP. *Indiana of the Northwest Coast*. New York: McGraw Hill Book Co., Inc., 1955.

FAINSOD, MERLE AND GORDON, LINCOLN. *Government and the American Economy*. New York: W. W. Norton and Co., Inc., 1941.

GRAHAM, MICHAEL. *The Fish Gate*. London: Faber and Faber, Ltd., 1949.

GREGORY, HOMER E., AND BARNES, KATHLEEN. *North Pacific Fisheries*. San Francisco: American Institute of Pacific Relations, 1939.

GRUENING, ERNEST. *The State of Alaska*. New York: Random House, 1954.

HAWTHORN, AUDREY. *People of the Potlatch*. Vancouver: University of British Columbia, 1956.

International Agreement on Conservation of Marine Resources, with Special Reference to the North Pacific. Food Research Institute, Stanford University, 1943.

KAPP, WILLIAM K. *The Social Costs of Private Enterprise*. Cambridge: Harvard University Press, 1950.

KRAUSE, AUREL. *The Tlingit Indian*. Seattle: University of Washington Press, 1956.

Liberate Alaska from the Fish Trap. Ketchikan, Alaska, 1949.

NICHOLS, J. P. *Alaska, A History of its First Half Century under the Rule of the United States*. Cleveland: Arthur H. Clark Co., 1924.

ROGERS, GEORGE W. *Alaska in Transition: The Southeast Region*. Baltimore: Johns Hopkins Press, 1960.

ROUNDSEFELL, GEORGE A. AND EVERHART, HARRY W. *Fishery Science: Its Methods and Applications*. New York: John Wiley and Sons, Inc., 1953.

RUSSELL, E. S. *The Overfishing Problem*. Cambridge: University of Cambridge Press, 1942.

UNITED NATIONS FOOD AND AGRICULTURAL ORGANIZATION. *The Economics of Fisheries; Proceedings of a Round Table Organized by the International Economic Association*. Rome: F.A.O., 1957.

WALFORD, L. A. *Living Resources of the Sea*. New York: The Ronald Press Co., 1958.

WICKERSHAM, J. *A Bibliography of Alaskan Literature, 1724-1924*. Fairbanks: University of Alaska, 1927.

GOVERNMENT REPORTS AND DOCUMENTS

ALASKA CONSTITUTIONAL CONVENTION. *The Constitution of the State of Alaska*. Fairbanks: University of Alaska, 1956.

ALASKA DEPARTMENT OF FISHERIES. *Annual Report*. Juneau: State of Alaska, 1949 to 1955.

ALASKA TERRITORIAL LEGISLATURE. *Alaska Senate Journal* (published biennially in Juneau), 1913 to 1959.

ALASKA TERRITORIAL LEGISLATURE. *Journal of the House of Representatives*. (published biennially in Juneau) 1913 to 1959.

ARNOLD, JOHN R. *Earnings of Fishermen and of Fishing Craft*. Washington: Office of National Recovery Administration, Division of Review, Work Materials No. 31, 1936.

BEAN, TARLETON H. *Report on the Salmon and Salmon Rivers of Alaska.* Bulletin of the U.S. Fish Commission. Washington: U.S. Government Printing Office, 1889.

CHAMBERLAIN, F. M. *Some Observations on Salmon and Trout in Alaska.* Bureau of Fisheries Document No. 627. Washington: U.S. Government Printing Office, 1907.

COBB, JOHN H. *Pacific Salmon Fisheries.* Bureau of Fisheries Document No. 1092. Washington: U.S. Government Printing Office, 1930.

COBB, J. H. *Pacific Salmon Fisheries.* Bureau of Fisheries Document 902, Washington: U.S. Government Printing Office, 1922 (3rd edition).

GILBERT, C. H. AND O'MALLEY, HENRY. *Investigations of the Salmon Fisheries of the Yukon River.* Bureau of Fisheries Document 909a. Washington: U.S. Government Printing Office, 1922.

GILBERT, C. H., AND O'MALLEY, HENRY. "Special Investigations of the Salmon Fishery in Central and Western Alaska." *Alaska Fishery and Fur-Seal Industries in 1919.* U.S. Bureau of Fisheries. Washington: U.S. Government Printing Office, 1920. 143-60.

JORDON, D. S., AND GILBERT, C. H. "The Salmon Fishing and Canning Interests of the Pacific Coast," *Report of the Fishing Industry of the United States.* Vol. 5. Washington: U.S. Government Printing Office, 1884.

MOSHER, JEFFERSON F. *The Salmon and the Salmon Fisheries of Alaska.* Washington: U.S. Government Printing Office, 1899.

MCDONALD, MARSHALL. *Report on the Salmon Fisheries of Alaska.* U.S. Fish Commission. Washington: U.S. Government Printing Office, 1892.

PETROFF, I. *History Resources and Trade of Alaska, Report on Internal Commerce.* Washington: U.S. Government Printing Office, 1890.

PETROFF, I. *Population, Industry and Resources of Alaska.* Washington: U.S. Government Printing Office, 1880.

PURDON, R. L. *World Trade in Canned Salmon.* Foreign and Domestic Commerce Bureau, Trade Promotion Series 14. Washington: U.S. Government Printing Office, 1925.

RICH, WILLIS H., AND BALL, EDWARD. *Statistical Review of the Alaska Salmon Fisheries.* Bureau of Fisheries Document 1041. Washington: U.S. Government Printing Office, 1928.

ROYCE, WILLIAM F. *Japanese Salmon Fishery.* U.S. Fish and Wildlife Service, Fishery Leaflet No. 230. Washington: U.S. Government Printing Office, 1947.

STATE OF ALASKA. *Session Laws of Alaska* (published biennially by the office of the Secretary of Alaska, Juneau), 1913 to 1959.

U.S. *Congressional Record.* Vol. 33 to Vol. 107.

U.S. CONGRESS, HOUSE, MERCHANT MARINE AND FISHERIES COMMITTEE. *Investigations of the Fisheries of Alaska, Preliminary Report Pursuant to H. Res. 162.* 76th Cong., 3rd Sess., 1940.

U.S. CONGRESS, HOUSE. *Preliminary Report of the Alaska Salmon Commission.* Document No. 477, 34th Cong., 2nd Sess., 1904.

U.S. CONGRESS, SENATE, COMMITTEE ON INTERSTATE AND FOREIGN COM-

MERCE. *Pacific Coast and Alaska Fisheries. Report . . . Pursuant to S. Res. 13 and S. Res. 163*. 84th Cong., 2nd Sess., 1956.

U.S. CONGRESS, SENATE, COMMITTEE ON INTERSTATE AND FOREIGN COMMERCE. *Program for the Rehabilitation of the Alaska Salmon Fisheries, Report Prepared . . . by Senator Warren G. Magnuson*. 84th Cong., 2nd Sess., 1956.

U.S. CONGRESS, SENATE, COMMITTEE ON COMMERCE. *Protection of Fisheries of Alaska, Report to Accompany H.R. 8143*. Senate Report No. 449. 68th Cong., 1st Sess., 1924.

U.S. DEPARTMENT OF AGRICULTURE, MARKETS BUREAU. *Supply of Canned Salmon in the United States, Its Extent and Distribution*. Circular No. 98. Washington: U.S. Government Printing Office, 1918.

U.S. DEPARTMENT OF COMMERCE AND LABOR. *Annual Report of the Secretary*. Washington: U.S. Government Printing Office, 1903 to 1912.

U.S. DEPARTMENT OF COMMERCE. *Annual Report of the Secretary*. Washington: U.S. Government Printing Office, 1913 to 1939.

U.S. DEPARTMENT OF COMMERCE, BUREAU OF FISHERIES, ALASKA FISHERIES SERVICE. *Alaska Fishery and Fur-Seal Industries* (annual). Washington: U.S. Government Printing Office, 1911 to 1939.

U.S. DEPARTMENT OF COMMERCE, BUREAU OF FISHERIES. *Annual Report of the Commissioner of Fisheries* (annual). Washington: U.S. Government Printing Office, 1911 to 1939.

U.S. DEPARTMENT OF COMMERCE, BUREAU OF FISHERIES. *The Fisheries of Alaska* (annual). Washington: U.S. Government Printing Office, 1904 to 1910.

U.S. DEPARTMENT OF THE INTERIOR. *Annual Report of the Governor of Alaska to the Secretary of the Interior*. Washington: U.S. Government Printing Office, 1885 to 1958.

U.S. DEPARTMENT OF THE INTERIOR. *Annual Report of the Secretary*. Washington: U.S. Government Printing Office, 1939 to 1959.

U.S. DEPARTMENT OF THE INTERIOR, FISH AND WILDLIFE SERVICE. *Alaska Fisheries 1959*. C.F.S. No. 2339. Washington: U.S. Government Printing Office, 1960. (Published annually since 1927.)

U.S. DEPARTMENT OF THE INTERIOR. FISH AND WILDLIFE SERVICE. *Alaska Fishery and Fur-Seal Industries*. (annual). Washington: U.S. Government Printing Office (annually from 1940 to 1956).

U.S. DEPARTMENT OF THE INTERIOR, FISH AND WILDLIFE SERVICE. *International North Pacific Fisheries Commission, United States Section Meeting, 1960*. Circular 85. Washington, 1960.

U.S. DEPARTMENT OF THE INTERIOR, FISH AND WILDLIFE SERVICE. *Laws and Regulations for Protection of the Commercial Fisheries of Alaska, 1958*. Regulatory Announcement 56. Washington: U.S. Government Printing Office, 1958. (Published annually since 1900.)

U.S. DEPARTMENT OF THE INTERIOR, FISH AND WILDLIFE SERVICE. *Progress Report on Alaska Fisheries Management and Research, 1958*. (Prepared by the staff at Juneau, Alaska, processed.) 1958.

U.S. Department of Justice. *Authority to Limit Trap Fishing in Alaska.* Opinions of the Attorney General, Vol. 40. Washington: U.S. Government Printing Office, 1942.

U.S. Department of the Treasury. *Seal and Salmon Fisheries and General Resources of Alaska.* Washington: U.S. Government Printing Office, 1898.

U.S. Department of the Treasury, Special Agents Division. *Report on Salmon Fisheries of Alaska* (annual). Washington: U.S. Government Printing Office, 1894 to 1904.

U.S. Federal Trade Commission. *Food Investigation: Report . . . on Canned Salmon.* Washington: U.S. Government Printing Office, 1919.

U.S. Fish Commission. *Annual Report of the Commissioner.* Washington: U.S. Government Printing Office, 1890 to 1903.

U.S. National Recovery Administration. *Hearings on the Codes of Fair Competition, Canned Salmon.* (Hearing No. 74.) Washington: U.S. Government Printing Office, 1934.

U.S. National Resources Committee. *Regional Planning, Part VII, Alaska—Its Resources and Development.* Washington: U.S. Government Printing Office, 1938.

U.S. Forest Service, Alaska Forest Research Center. *Physical Effects of Logging on Salmon Streams of Southeast Alaska.* Station Paper No. 5. (Processed.) 1956.

U.S. Tariff Commission. *Report to the United States Senate on Salmon and other Fish.* Report No. 121 (2nd Series). Washington: U.S. Government Printing Office, 1937.

Walford, Lionel A. *Fishery Resources of the United States of America.* Fish and Wildlife Service, U.S. Department of the Interior. Washington: U.S. Government Printing Office, 1945.

CONGRESSIONAL HEARINGS
(Listed Chronologically)

U.S. Congress, House, Committee on the Territories. *Fisheries in Alaska, Hearings.* 59th Cong., 1st Sess., 1906.

U.S. Congress, House, Committee on the Territories. *Amendment of Laws Relating to Fisheries and Other Occupations in Alaska, Hearings.* 61st Cong., 2nd Sess., 1910.

U.S. Congress, Senate, Committee on Fisheries. *Alaska Fisheries, Hearings . . . on S. 5856.* 62nd Cong., 2nd Sess., 1912.

U.S. Congress, House, Committee on Merchant Marine and Fisheries. *Alaska Fisheries, Hearings on H.R. 9528.* 64th Cong., 1st Sess., 1916.

U.S. Congress, House, Committee on the Territories. *Bill to Repeal Law Allowing Alaska to Tax the Fisheries, Hearings on H.R. 9527.* 64th Cong., 1st Sess., 1916.

U.S. Congress, House, Merchant Marine and Fisheries Committee.

Alaska Fisheries, Hearings on H.R. 9092 for Regulation and Prohibition. 65th Cong., 2nd Sess., 1918.

U.S. Congress, House, Merchant Marine and Fisheries Committee. *Hearing . . . on a Bill to Prohibit Fishing for Salmon in the Yukon River.* 66th Cong., 2nd Sess., 1920.

U.S. Congress, House, Merchant Marine and Fisheries Committee. *Fisheries in Alaska, Hearings on H.R. 2394.* 67th Cong., 1st Sess., 1921.

U.S. Congress, House, Merchant Marine and Fisheries Committee. *Fisheries in Alaska, Hearings on H.R. 2394.* (2 pts.) 67th Cong., 1st Sess., 1921, 1922.

U.S. Congress, House, Merchant Marine and Fisheries Committee. *Fisheries of Alaska, Hearings on H.R. 2714.* 68th Cong., 1st Sess., 1924.

U.S. Congress, House, Merchant Marine and Fisheries Committee. *Alaskan Canneries, Hearings . . . on H.R. 13534.* 71st Cong., 3rd Sess., 1930.

U.S. Congress, House, Merchant Marine and Fisheries Committee. *Protection of Alaskan Fisheries, Hearings . . . on H.R. 253 and H.R. 7238.* 71st Cong., 2nd Sess., 1930.

U.S. Congress, House, Merchant Marine, Radio and Fisheries Committee. *Alaskan Canneries, Hearings . . . on H.R. 6483.* 72nd Cong., 1st Sess., 1932.

U.S. Congress, Senate, Committee on Commerce. *Protection and Regulation of the Alaska Fisheries, Hearings . . . Pursuant to S. 3379.* 72nd Cong., 2nd Sess., 1933.

U.S. Congress, House, Merchant Marine, Radio and Fisheries Committee. *Alaskan Fisheries, Hearings . . . on H.R. 6175 and H.R. 7523.* 73rd Cong., 2nd Sess., 1934.

U.S. Congress, House, Merchant Marine, Radio and Fisheries Committee. *Jurisdiction of Alaska Fisheries, Hearing . . . on H.R. 5205.* 73rd. Cong., 2nd Sess., 1934.

U.S. Congress, House, Merchant Marine and Fisheries Committee. *Fish Traps in Alaskan Waters, Hearings . . . on H.R. 4254 and H.R. 8213.* 74th Cong., 2nd Sess., 1936.

U.S. Congress, House, Merchant Marine and Fisheries Committee. *Alaska Salmon Fishery, Hearings . . . on H.R. 8344.* 75th Cong., 3rd Sess., 1938.

U.S. Congress, House, Committee on Merchant Marine and Fisheries. *Committee Study Resolution—Alaska Fisheries Hearings . . . Pursuant to H.R. 162.* 76th Cong., 1st Sess. 1939.

U.S. Congress, House, Merchant Marine and Fisheries Committee. *Alaskan Fisheries, Hearings on . . . H.R. 5478 and Other Bills.* 76th Cong., 3rd Sess., 1940.

U.S. Congress, House, Merchant Marine and Fisheries Committee. *Alaskan Fisheries, Hearings . . . Pursuant to H. Res. 162.* 76th Cong., 3rd Sess., 1940.

U.S. Congress, Senate, Committee on Commerce. *Alaska Fisheries Act, Hearings . . . on S. 930.* 78th Cong., 2nd Sess., 1944.

U.S. Congress, House, Merchant Marine and Fisheries Committee. *Alaska Fisheries Hearings . . . Pursuant to H. Res. 38.* 79th Cong., 2nd Sess., 1946.

U.S. Congress, Senate, Interstate and Foreign Commerce Committee. *Leasing of Salmon Trap Sites, Hearings . . . on S. 1446.* 80th Cong., 1st Sess., 1947. (2 pts.)

U.S. Congress, House, Merchant Marine and Fisheries Committee. *Elimination of Salmon Traps in the Waters of Alaska, Hearings . . . on H.R. 1515.* 81st Cong., 1st Sess., 1949.

U.S. Congress, House, Interior and Insular Affairs Committee. *Transfer, Jurisdiction, Supervision, Administration and Control of Fisheries of Alaska to the Territory of Alaska, Hearings . . . on H.R. 7648.* 82nd Cong., 2nd Sess., 1952.

U.S. Congress, House, Interstate and Foreign Commerce Committee. *Pacific Coast and Alaska Fisheries, Hearings . . . Pursuant to S. Res. 13.* 84th Cong., 2nd Sess., 1955.

U.S. Congress, House, Committee on Territorial and Insular Affairs. *Hearings . . . Pursuant to H. Res. 30.* 84th Cong., 1st Sess., 1955.

ARTICLES AND PERIODICALS

Ackerman, Edward. "Conservation and Control of Pacific Fisheries," *Far Eastern Survey,* XV (January 1946), 8-9.

Allen, E. W. "The North Pacific Fisheries," *Pacific Affairs,* X (June 1937), 136-51.

Barnes, Kathleen and Gregory, H. E. "Alaska Salmon in World Politics," *Far Eastern Survey,* VII (March 1938), 47-53.

Barnes, Kathleen, "The Clash of Fishing Interests in the Pacific," *Far Eastern Survey,* V (November 1936), 243-247.

Brown, W. G. "The Death Knell of Alaska Salmon," *American Forests,* XXXI (March 1932), 159-162.

Canadian Western Fisheries, Vols. I to LV.

Crutchfield, James A. "Common Property Resources and Factor Allocation," *Canadian Journal of Economics and Political Science,* XXII (August 1956), 292-300.

De Loach, Barton. "Important Factors Affecting the Marketing of Salmon," *American Marketing Journal,* II (October 1935), 253-264.

Elson, P. E. and Kersevill, C. J. "Problems of Pacific Salmon Management," *North American Wildlife Conference Transactions,* 1955, 426-440.

Freeman, O. W. "Salmon Industry of the Pacific Coast," *Economic Geography,* XI (April 1935), 109-129.

Gladstone, Percy. "Native Indians and the Fishing Industry of British Columbia, Indian Participation and Technological Adoption," *Canadian Journal of Economics and Political Science,* IXX (February 1953), 20-34.

GREGORY, H. E. "Salmon Industry of the Pacific Coast," *Economic Geography,* XVI (October 1940), 407-415.

GRUENING, ERNEST. "The Political Ecology of Alaska," *Scientific Monthly,* December 1951, 376-386.

HAIG-BROWN, R. L. "Canada's Pacific Salmon," *Canadian Geography Journal,* XLIV (March 1952), 109-127.

JESSUP, P. C. "The Pacific Coast Fisheries," *American Journal of International Law,* XXXIII (January 1939), 129-138.

Pacific Fisherman. Vols. I to LVIII.

PRYCE-TANNATT, T. E. "Laws and Regulations in Summary Concerning Salmon and Trout Fisheries," *Rapports et Procès—Verbaux des Reunions,* Vol. 96, Conseil Permanent International pour L'Exploration de la Mer, February 1936.

RANDALL, R. L. "Labor Agreements in the West Coast Fishing Industry," *Industrial Labor Relations Review.* III (July 1950), 514-41.

"Salmon, An Industry Conserved," *Commerce Monthly.* New York: National Bank of Commerce, January 1927.

"The Law of Fish and Fisheries," *American Jurisprudence.* Vol. 22. San Francisco: Bancroft-Whitney Co., 1939 (with annual supplements), 666-709.

THOMPSON, SETON H. "Management of the Marine Resources of Alaska," *Science in Alaska.* Washington: Arctic Institute of North America, 1952.

UNPUBLISHED MATERIAL

ALVERSON, DAYTON L. *Report from the International World Fishing Gear Congress.* Hamburg, Germany, October 1957. (Mimeographed.)

BALTZO, C. HOWARD. *Fisheries Industries of Alaska and Their Administration.* U.S. Fish and Wildlife Service, Leaflet 322. (Processed.) 1948.

BALTZO, C. HOWARD. "Federal Administration of the Fishery Industries of Alaska." Juneau, Alaska, 1958. (Mimeographed.)

CRUTCHFIELD, JAMES A. "An Economic Evaluation of Alternative Methods of Fishery Regulations," University of Washington, 1960. (Mimeographed.)

CRUTCHFIELD, JAMES A. "The Economics of Salmon Management." Unpublished paper delivered at the Alaska Science Conference, Juneau, Alaska, August 1959. (Mimeographed.)

HEWES, GORDON. "Aboriginal Use of Fishery Resources in Northwest North America." Unpublished Ph.D. dissertation, University of California, 1957. (Processed.)

MINGHI, JULIAN VINCENT. "The Conflict of Salmon Fishing Policies in the Pacific Northwest." Seattle: University of Washington, Department of Geography, Discussion Paper No. 27. October 1959. (Mimeographed.)

ROYCE, WILLIAM A. "Fishery Regulation in Alaska Salmon Management." Fisheries Research Institute, Circular No. 123. Seattle: University of Washington, 1961. (Mimeographed.)

U.S. NATIONAL RECOVERY ADMINISTRATION, DIVISION OF REVIEW, INDUSTRY STUDIES SECTION. *The Fishery Industry and the Fishery Code.* Work Materials No. 31, January 1936. (Mimeographed.)

Index

About the Author

Richard A. Cooley went to Alaska in 1951 shortly after graduating from the University of New Mexico. For three years he was employed by the territorial government as a research assistant with the Alaska Resources Development Board. While with the Board he completed a series of economic and resource studies which took him to various sections of Alaska.

He received a Master's degree from the University of Chicago in 1956 and took his Ph.D. from the School of Natural Resources at the University of Michigan.

Shortly after Alaska became a state, Dr. Cooley returned there to establish a small private research center with a grant from The Conservation Foundation of New York City. During the past four years he has been engaged in foundation-sponsored research directed toward problems of natural resource development and conservation which confront the new state, and he has served as an economic consultant to various state and federal agencies.

Dr. Cooley lives in Juneau with his wife and two sons, where he is director of the Alaska Natural Resources Research Center.

Format by Mort Perry
Set in Linotype Caledonia
Composed by The Haddon Craftsmen, Inc.
Printed by Murray Printing Company
Bound by The Haddon Craftsmen, Inc.
HARPER & ROW, PUBLISHERS, INCORPORATED